SCIENCE

TEXTBOOK FOR CLASS VII

 W9-CQQ-523

Our National Flag

The Indian National Flag is the symbol of the land and people of India. Our National Flag is a tricolour panel made up of three rectangular panels or sub-panels of equal widths. The colour of the top panel is India saffron *(Kesaria)* and that of the bottom is India green. The middle panel is white, bearing at its centre the design of the Ashoka Chakra in navy blue colour with 24 equally spaced spokes. The Ashoka Chakra is visible on both sides of the Flag in the centre of the white panel. The Flag is rectangular in shape with the ratio of the length to the height (width) being 3 : 2.

Dr S. Radhakrishnan explained about the National Flag in the Constituent Assembly which adopted it, "Bhagwa or the saffron colour denotes renunciation or disinterestedness. The white in the centre is light, the path of truth to guide our conduct. The green shows our relation to the soil, our relation to the plant life here on which all other life depends. The Ashoka Wheel is the wheel of the law of dharma. Truth or *satya*, dharma or virtue ought to be the controlling principles of those who work under this flag. Again, the wheel denotes motion. There is life in movement. India must move and go forward."

If done properly, there is no restriction on the display of the National Flag by common people, private organisations or educational institutions. Consistent with the dignity and honour of the Flag as detailed in the Flag Code of India, anyone may hoist/display the National Flag on all days and occasions, ceremonial or otherwise.

Where the practice is to fly the Flag on any public building, it must be flown on the building on all days including Sundays and holidays and, except as provided in the Code, it shall be flown from sunrise to sunset irrespective of weather conditions. The Flag may be flown on such a building at night also but this should be only on very special occasions.

The Flag must not be used as a drapery in any form except in State/Military/Central Paramilitary Forces funerals. In such cases also the Flag must not be lowered into the grave or burnt in the pyre. The Flag must not be draped over the hood, top, sides or back of a vehicle, train or boat. It must not be used or stored in such a manner as may damage or soil it. When the Flag is in a damaged or soiled condition, it must not be cast aside or disrespectfully disposed of but be destroyed as a whole in private, preferably by burning. The Flag must not be used as a covering for a building. Although the Flag can be used as a costume or uniform, it should not be used as undergarments or below the waist. It must not be embroidered or printed upon cushions, napkins, etc. Lettering of any kind must not be put upon the Flag. It must not be used in any form of advertisement. Showing disrespect or insult to the National Flag is a punishable offence.

The National Flag must not be flown from a single masthead simultaneously with any other flag. There must be separate mastheads for different flags. When a foreign dignitary travels in a car provided by Government, the National Flag is flown on the right side of the car and the Flag of the foreign countries on the left side of the car.

In the event of the death of the President, the Vice-President or the Prime Minister, the National Flag is half-masted throughout the country.

Over the last five decades, several people including members of the armed forces have laid down their lives to keep the tricolour flying in its full glory. We must salute and cherish our National Flag.

SCIENCE

TEXTBOOK FOR CLASS VII

राष्ट्रीय शैक्षिक अनुसंधान और प्रशिक्षण परिषद्
NATIONAL COUNCIL OF EDUCATIONAL RESEARCH AND TRAINING

ISBN 81-7450-654-3

First Edition
January 2007 Magha 1928

Reprinted
November 2007 Kartika 1929
January 2009 Pausa 1930
January 2010 Magha 1931
January 2011 Magha 1932
January 2012 Magha 1933
December 2012 Agrahayana 1934

PD 700T BS

© *National Council of Educational Research and Training, 2007*

₹ **50.00**

Printed on 80 GSM paper with NCERT watermark

Published at the Publication Division by the Secretary, National Council of Educational Research and Training, Sri Aurobindo Marg New Delhi 110 016 and printed at Pankaj Printing Press, D-28, Industrial Area, Site-A, Mathura 281 004 (Uttar Pradesh)

ALL RIGHTS RESERVED

- No part of this publication may be reproduced, stored in a retrieval system or transmitted, in any form or by any means, electronic, mechanical, photocopying, recording or otherwise without the prior permission of the publisher.

- This book is sold subject to the condition that it shall not, by way of trade, be lent, re-sold, hired out or otherwise disposed of without the publisher's consent, in any form of binding or cover other than that in which it is published.

- The correct price of this publication is the price printed on this page, Any revised price indicated by a rubber stamp or by a sticker or by any other means is incorrect and should be unacceptable.

OFFICES OF THE PUBLICATION DIVISION, NCERT

NCERT Campus
Sri Aurobindo Marg
New Delhi 110 016   Phone : 011-26562708

108, 100 Feet Road
Hosdakere Halli Extension
Banashankari III Stage
Bangalore 560 085   Phone : 080-26725740

Navjivan Trust Building
P.O.Navjivan
Ahmedabad 380 014   Phone : 079-27541446

CWC Campus
Opp. Dhankal Bus Stop
Panihati
Kolkata 700 114   Phone : 033-25530454

CWC Complex
Maligaon
Guwahati 781 021   Phone : 0361-2674869

Publication Team

Head, Publication Division	: *Ashok Srivastava*
Chief Production Officer	: *Shiv Kumar*
Chief Editor (Incharge)	: *Naresh Yadav*
Chief Business Manager	: *Gautam Ganguly*
Editor	: *Bijnan Sutar*
Production Officer	: *Arun Chitkara*

Cover, Layout and Illustrations

Ashwani Tyagi

FOREWORD

The National Curriculum Framework (NCF), 2005, recommends that children's life at school must be linked to their life outside the school. This principle marks a departure from the legacy of bookish learning which continues to shape our system and causes a gap between the school, home and community. The syllabi and textbooks developed on the basis of NCF signify an attempt to implement this basic idea. They also attempt to discourage rote learning and the maintenance of sharp boundaries between different subject areas. We hope these measures will take us significantly further in the direction of a child-centred system of education outlined in the National Policy on Education (1986).

The success of this effort depends on the steps that school principals and teachers will take to encourage children to reflect on their own learning and to pursue imaginative activities and questions. We must recognise that, given space, time and freedom, children generate new knowledge by engaging with the information passed on to them by adults. Treating the prescribed textbook as the sole basis of examination is one of the key reasons why other resources and sites of learning are ignored. Inculcating creativity and initiative is possible if we perceive and treat children as participants in learning, not as receivers of a fixed body of knowledge.

These aims imply considerable change in school routines and mode of functioning. Flexibility in the daily time-table is as necessary as rigour in implementing the annual calendar so that the required number of teaching days are actually devoted to teaching. The methods used for teaching and evaluation will also determine how effective this textbook proves for making children's life at school a happy experience, rather than a source of stress or boredom. Syllabus designers have tried to address the problem of curricular burden by restructuring and reorienting knowledge at different stages with greater consideration for child psychology and the time available for teaching. The textbook attempts to enhance this endeavour by giving higher priority and space to opportunities for contemplation and wondering, discussion in small groups, and activities requiring hands-on experience.

The National Council of Educational Research and Training (NCERT) appreciates the hard work done by the Textbook Development Committee responsible for this book. We wish to thank the Chairperson of the advisory group in Science and Mathematics, Professor J.V. Narlikar and the Chief Advisor for this book, Prof. V.B. Bhatia for guiding the work of this committee. Several teachers contributed to the development of this textbook; we are grateful to their principals for making this possible. We are indebted to the institutions and organisations which have generously permitted us to draw upon their resources, material and personnel. We are especially grateful to the members of the National Monitoring Committee, iv

appointed by the Department of Secondary and Higher Education, Ministry of Human Resource Development under the Chairpersonship of Professor Mrinal Miri and Professor G.P. Deshpande, for their valuable time and contribution. As an organisation committed to systemic reform and continuous improvement in the quality of its products, the NCERT welcomes comments and suggestions which will enable us to undertake further revision and refinement.

Director
National Council of Educational
Research and Training

New Delhi
20 November 2006

PREFACE

This book is the outcome of the efforts of the Textbook Development Committee appointed by the NCERT. The committee met a few times to interact with one another to improve the draft. Then there was a review meeting in which many experts and practicing school teachers were invited to review the draft and suggest improvements.

By and large we have stuck to the format of the Class VI book. By now, famous characters, Boojho and Paheli, have been used to make the text interactive. Attempt has been made to recall children's own experiences and build concepts around them. This is designed to connect science that they study in the school with their every-day life.

Many activities have been suggested to clarify concepts. Some of these activities are so simple that children can perform them on their own. The requirement of the apparatus required for the activities is minimal. We performed all the activities ourselves to ensure that there was no difficulty in performing them in the school situation. The activities should also help children in developing skills such as presentation of data in tabular and graphical forms, reasoning and drawing inference from the given data.

The language of the book has been kept as simple as possible. A large number of photographs, illustrations, cartoons, etc. have been included to make the book attractive. To help teachers evaluate children effectively, a large number of exercises have been given at the end of each chapter. The teachers are encouraged to frame additional exercises to test children's understanding. Some challenging exercises have also been devised for those children who would like to appear for the National Talent Search Examination conducted by the NCERT.

We are conscious of the fact that there is a paucity of additional reading material for children. We have tried to address this problem by providing **non-evaluative boxes**. These boxes, in blue, contain additional information, anecdotes, stories, strange facts and other such interesting materials.

We all know that children are mischievous and playful by nature. Therefore, in order to prevent any untoward incident during the performance of the activities in the school or outside, necessary cautions, in red, have been inserted at various places in the book.

To prepare children to assume their roles as responsible citizens of tomorrow, attempt has been made to sensitise them to the issues concerning gender, religion, environment, health and hygiene, water scarcity and energy conservation. We have sought to weave into the text the value of cooperation and the importance of peer learning.

An important feature of the book is what we call **'Extended Learning'**. These are totally **non-evaluative**, and purely voluntary activities and projects. Some of the projects in this section have been designed to enhance children's interaction with the experts, teachers, even parents, and society at large. The children are required to collect information of various kind and draw conclusions of their own.

My request to teachers and parents is to use the book in the spirit in which it has been written. Encourage children to perform activities and learn by doing, rather than by rote.

You can supplement, or even replace, the activities given here. If you feel that you have better alternatives, especially with your local/regional flavour, please write to us so that these activities could be used in the future editions of the book.

We have been able to include only a small subset of children's experiences. You have a better knowledge of their experiences because you are in touch with them. Use them to illustrate the concepts being taught. Above all, please do not stifle children's natural curiosity. Encourage them to ask questions, even if sometimes you feel uncomfortable. If you do not know the answer to a question on the spot, do not feel embarrassed. You can promise them to find the answer and deal with it later. Make a genuine attempt to get the answer from whatever resources are within your reach, such as senior school or college teachers, experts, libraries, internet, etc. If, in spite of your efforts, you cannot get the answer to some question, you could write to NCERT.

I must thank the NCERT for enabling us to talk to children through the medium of this book. Every member of the NCERT has been courteous and helpful to us. If you find this book useful and enjoy teaching/learning science through this book, the Editing Team and I shall consider ourselves well-rewarded.

V.B. BHATIA
Chief Advisor
Textbook Development Committee

TEXTBOOK DEVELOPMENT COMMITTEE

CHAIRPERSON, ADVISORY GROUP FOR TEXTBOOKS IN SCIENCE AND MATHEMATICS

J.V. Narlikar, *Emeritus Professor*, Inter University Centre for Astronomy and Astrophysics (IUCCA), Ganeshkhind, Pune University, Pune

CHIEF ADVISOR

V.B. Bhatia, *Professor*, Retd. *(Physics)*, Delhi University, Delhi

MEMBERS

Bharati Sarkar, *Reader*, Retd. *(Zoology)*, Maitreyi College, Delhi University, Delhi

C.V. Shimray, *Lecturer*, Department of Education in Science and Mathematics (DESM), NCERT, Sri Aurobindo Marg, New Delhi

D. Lahiry, *Professor*, Retd, DESM, NCERT, Sri Aurobindo Marg, New Delhi

G.P. Pande, Uttarakhand Seva Nidhi, Paryavaran Shiksha Sansthan, Jakhan Devi, Almora, Uttaranchal

Harsh Kumari, *Headmistress*, CIE Experimental Basic School, Department of Education, Delhi University, Delhi

J.S. Gill, *Professor*, DESM, NCERT, Sri Aurobindo Marg, New Delhi

Kamal Deep Peter, *TGT (Science)*, Kendriya Vidyalaya, Bangalore

Kanhiya Lal, *Principal*, Retd., Directorate of Education, Delhi

Lalita S. Kumar, *Reader (Chemistry)*, School of Sciences, Indira Gandhi National Open University (IGNOU), Maidan Garhi, New Delhi

Mohd. Iftikhar Alam, *TGT (Science)*, Sarvodaya Bal Vidyalaya (No.1), Jama Masjid, Delhi

P.S. Yadava, *Professor*, Department of Life Sciences, Manipur University, Imphal

R. Joshi, *Lecturer* (Selection Grade), DESM, NCERT, Sri Aurobindo Marg, New Delhi

Rachna Garg, *Lecturer*, Central Institute of Educational Technology, NCERT, Sri Aurobindo Marg, New Delhi

Ranjana Agrawal, *Principal Scientist and Head*, Division of Forecasting Techniques, Indian Agricultural Statistics Research Institute, IARI Campus, Pusa, New Delhi

R.S. Sindhu, *Professor*, DESM, NCERT, Sri Aurobindo Marg, New Delhi

Ruchi Verma, *Lecturer*, PPMED, NCERT, Sri Aurobindo Marg, New Delhi

Sarita Kumar, *Reader (Zoology)*, Acharya Narendra Dev College, Delhi University, Delhi

Sunila Masih, *Teacher*, Mitra GHS School, Suhagpur, P.O. Hoshangabad, Madhya Pradesh

V.K. Gupta, *Reader (Chemistry)*, Hans Raj College, Delhi University, Delhi

MEMBER-COORDINATOR

R.K. Parashar, *Lecturer*, DESM, NCERT, Sri Aurobindo Marg, New Delhi

THE CONSTITUTION OF INDIA

PREAMBLE

WE, THE PEOPLE OF INDIA, having solemnly resolved to constitute India into a **SOVEREIGN SOCIALIST SECULAR DEMOCRATIC REPUBLIC** and to secure to all its citizens :

JUSTICE, social, economic and political;

LIBERTY of thought, expression, belief, faith and worship;

EQUALITY of status and of opportunity; and to promote among them all

FRATERNITY assuring the dignity of the individual and the unity and integrity of the Nation;

IN OUR CONSTITUENT ASSEMBLY this twenty-sixth day of November, 1949, do **HEREBY ADOPT, ENACT AND GIVE TO OURSELVES THIS CONSTITUTION.**

ACKNOWLEDGEMENTS

The National Council of Educational Research and Training (NCERT) acknowledges the valuable contribution of the individuals and organisations involved in the development of Science textbook for Class VII. The Council acknowledges the valuable contribution of the following academics for reviewing and refining the manuscripts of this book: Sushma Kiran Setia, *Principal*, Sarvodaya Kanya Vidyalaya, Hari Nagar (Clock Tower), New Delhi; Mohini Bindra, *Principal*, Ramjas School, Pusa Road, New Delhi; D.K. Bedi, *Principal*, Apeejay Senior Secondary School, Pitampura, Road No. 42, Sainik Vihar, New Delhi; Chand Vir Singh, *Lecturer (Biology)*, GBSS School, Rajouri Garden (Main), New Delhi; Renuka Madan, *TGT (Physics)*, Air Force Golden Jubilee Institute, Subroto Park, Delhi Cantt; Reena Jhani, *TGT (Science)*, Darbari Lal DAV Model School, Pitam Pura, New Delhi; Geeta Bajaj, *TGT (Science)*, K. V. No. 3, Delhi Cantt., New Delhi; Gagandeep Bajaj, *Lecturer*, Department of Education, S.P.M. College, Delhi University, Delhi; Shashi Prabha, *Lecturer*, DESM, NCERT, New Delhi; A.K. Bakhshi, *Professor*, Department of Chemistry, University of Delhi, Delhi; N. Rathnasree, *Director*, Nehru Planetarium, Teen Murti Bhavan, New Delhi; S.B. Singh, *TGT (Science)*, J.N.V. Sonikpur, P.O. Trivediganj, Distt. Barabanki, Uttar Pradesh; Madhur Mohan Ranga, *Lecturer* (Selection Scale), *(Zoology)*, Govt. College, Ajmer, Rajasthan; K.G. Ojha, *Associate Professor*, Department of Chemistry, M.D.S. University, Ajmer, Rajasthan; Puneeta Sharma, *TGT (Science)*, L.D. Jain Girls Senior Secondary School, Pahari Dhiraj, Delhi; Manohar Lal Patel, *Teacher*, Govt. R.N.A. Exc. H.S.S. Pipariya, Distt. Hoshangabad, Madhya Pradesh; Bharat Bhushan Gupta, *PGT (Biology)*, Sarvodaya Vidyalaya, No.1, Shakurpur, Delhi; Sushma Jairath, *Reader*, Department of Women Studies (DWS), NCERT, New Delhi; Mina Yadav, *Lecturer*, DWS, NCERT, New Delhi; Swadesh Taneja, *Ex-Reader (Life Sciences)*, IGNOU, New Delhi and M.M. Kapur, *Professor*, Retd. *(Chemistry)*, Delhi University, Delhi.

The council is highly thankful to the India Meteorological Department, New Delhi, for providing some illustrations for the Chapter 8: Winds, Storms and Cyclones. The Council gratefully acknowledges the valuable suggestions received from the *National Monitoring Committee* in the development of the manuscript of this textbook.

The dynamic leadership of Professor Hukum Singh, *Head*, DESM, for providing guidance in the final editing of the manuscript and extending infrastructure facilities is highly acknowledged. Special thanks are due to Shveta Uppal, *Chief Editor*; and Bijnan Sutar, *Assistant Editor*, for going through the manuscript and suggesting relevant changes.

The Council also acknowledges the efforts of Deepak Kapoor, *Incharge*, Computer Station; Purnendu Kumar Barik, Musarrat Parveen and Satish Kumar Mishra, *Copy Editors;* Neelam Walecha and Muhammad Aiyub, *DTP Operators;* and Randhir Thakur, *Proof Reader.*

The contribution of APC-office, administration of DESM, Publication Department and Secretariat of NCERT is also acknowledged.

A NOTE FOR THE STUDENTS

The team of Paheli and Boojho will be with you as you journey through this textbook. They love to ask questions. All kind of questions come to their minds and they collect them in their sacks. Sometimes, they may share some of these questions with you, as you read through the chapters.

Paheli and Boojho are also on the lookout for answers to many questions — sometimes the questions seem answered after they discuss them with each other, sometimes through discussions with other classmates, teachers or their parents. Answers to some questions do not seem available even after all these. They might need to experiment on their own, read books in the library, send questions to scientists. Just dig and dig and dig into all possibilities and see if the questions can be answered. Perhaps, they would carry some of the unanswered questions in their sacks to higher classes.

What will really thrill them would be your adding questions to their sacks or answers to their questions. Sometimes, activities are suggested in the textbook, results or findings of these by different groups of students would be of interest to other students and teachers. You can complete the suggested activities and send your results or findings to Paheli and Boojho. Do keep in mind that activities that involve using blades, scissors or fire need to be done strictly under the care of your teachers. Stick to the precautions given and then enjoy doing all the suggested activities. Mind, the book will not be able to help you much, if the activities are not completed!

We would like to advise you that you must make observations yourself and record whatever results you get. Keen and true observations are necessary for exploring any subject of study. For some reason your results may turn out to be different from those of your classmates. Do not worry. Try to find out the reason for these results instead of disregarding them. Do not ever copy results from your classmate.

You can send your feedback for Paheli and Boojho at:

To

The Head
Department of Education in
Science and Mathematics,
NCERT, Sri Aurobindo Marg,
New Delhi 110 016

CONSTITUTION OF INDIA

Part IV A (Article 51 A)

Fundamental Duties

Fundamental Duties – It shall be the duty of every citizen of India —

(a) to abide by the Constitution and respect its ideals and institutions, the National Flag and the National Anthem;

(b) to cherish and follow the noble ideals which inspired our national struggle for freedom;

(c) to uphold and protect the sovereignty, unity and integrity of India;

(d) to defend the country and render national service when called upon to do so;

(e) to promote harmony and the spirit of common brotherhood amongst all the people of India transcending religious, linguistic and regional or sectional diversities; to renounce practices derogatory to the dignity of women;

(f) to value and preserve the rich heritage of our composite culture;

(g) to protect and improve the natural environment including forests, lakes, rivers, wildlife and to have compassion for living creatures;

(h) to develop the scientific temper, humanism and the spirit of inquiry and reform;

(i) to safeguard public property and to abjure violence;

(j) to strive towards excellence in all spheres of individual and collective activity so that the nation constantly rises to higher levels of endeavour and achievement;

(k) who is a parent or guardian, to provide opportunities for education to his child or, as the case may be, ward between the age of six and fourteen years.

CONTENTS

1 Nutrition in Plants

In Class VI you learnt that food is essential for all living organisms. You also learnt that carbohydrates, proteins, fats, vitamins and minerals are components of food. These components of food are necessary for our body and are called **nutrients**.

All living organisms require food. Plants can make their food themselves but animals including humans cannot. They get it from plants or animals that eat plants. Thus, humans and animals are directly or indirectly dependent on plants.

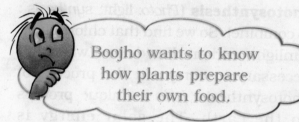

Boojho wants to know how plants prepare their own food.

1.1 MODE OF NUTRITION IN PLANTS

Plants are the only organisms that can prepare food for themselves by using water, carbon dioxide and minerals. The raw materials are present in their surroundings.

The nutrients enable living organisms to build their bodies, to grow, to repair damaged parts of their bodies and provide the energy to carry out life processes. **Nutrition** is the mode of taking food by an organism and its utilisation by the body. The mode of nutrition in which organisms make food themselves from simple substances is called **autotrophic** (*auto* = self; *trophos* = nourishment) nutrition. Therefore, plants are called **autotrophs**. Animals and most other organisms take in ready made food prepared by the plants. They are called **heterotrophs** (*heteros* = other).

Paheli wants to know why our body cannot make food from carbon dioxide, water and minerals like plants do.

Now we may ask where the food factories of plants are located: whether food is made in all parts of a plant or only in certain parts? How do plants obtain the raw materials from the surroundings? How do they transport them to the food factories of the plants?

1.2 PHOTOSYNTHESIS — FOOD MAKING PROCESS IN PLANTS

Leaves are the food factories of plants. The synthesis of food in plants occurs in leaves. Therefore, all the raw materials must reach there. Water and minerals present in the soil are absorbed by the roots and transported to the

Cells

You have seen that buildings are made of bricks. Similarly, the bodies of living organisms are made of tiny units called **cells**. Cells can be seen only under the microscope. Some organisms are made of only one cell. The cell is enclosed by a thin outer boundary, called the **cell membrane**. Most cells have a distinct, centrally located spherical structure called the **nucleus** (Fig. 1.1). The nucleus is surrounded by a jelly-like substance called **cytoplasm**.

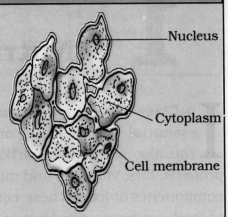

Fig. 1.1 Cell

leaves. Carbon dioxide from air is taken in through the tiny pores present on the surface of the leaves. These pores are surrounded by 'guard cells'. Such pores are called **stomata** [Fig. 1.2 (c)].

> Boojho wants to know how water and minerals absorbed by roots reach the leaves.

Water and minerals are transported to the leaves by the vessels which run like pipes throughout the root, the stem, the branches and the leaves. They form a continuous path or passage for the nutrients to reach the leaf. You will learn about transport of materials in plants in Chapter 11.

> Paheli wants to know what is so special about the leaves that they can synthesise food but other parts of the plant cannot.

The leaves have a **green pigment** called **chlorophyll**. It helps leaves to capture the energy of the sunlight. This energy is used to synthesise (prepare) food from carbon dioxide and water. Since the synthesis of food occurs in the presence of sunlight, it is called **photosynthesis** (*Photo*: light; *synthesis* : to combine). So we find that chlorophyll, sunlight, carbon dioxide and water are necessary to carry out the process of photosynthesis. It is a unique process on the earth. The solar energy is captured by the leaves and stored in the plant in the form of food. **Thus, sun is the ultimate source of energy for all living organisms**.

Can you imagine life on earth in the absence of photosynthesis!

In the absence of photosynthesis there would not be any food. The survival of almost all living organisms directly or indirectly depends upon the food made by the plants. Besides, oxygen which is essential for the survival

Besides leaves, photosynthesis also takes place in other green parts of the plant — in green stems and green branches. The desert plants have scale- or spine-like leaves to reduce loss of water by transpiration. These plants have green stems which carry out photosynthesis.

of all living organisms is produced during photosynthesis. In the absence of photosynthesis, life would be impossible on the earth.

During photosynthesis, chlorophyll containing cells of leaves (Fig. 1.2), in the presence of sunlight, use carbon dioxide and water to synthesise carbohydrates (Fig. 1.3). The process can be represented as an equation:

Carbon dioxide + water $\xrightarrow[\text{chlorophyll}]{\text{sunlight}}$

Carbohydrate + oxygen

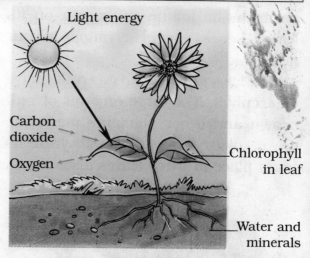

Fig. 1.3 Diagram showing photosynthesis

During the process oxygen is released. The carbohydrates ultimately get converted into starch. The presence of starch in leaves indicates the occurrence of photosynthesis. The starch is also a carbohydrate.

Boojho has observed some plants with deep red, violet or brown leaves. He wants to know whether these leaves also carry out photosynthesis.

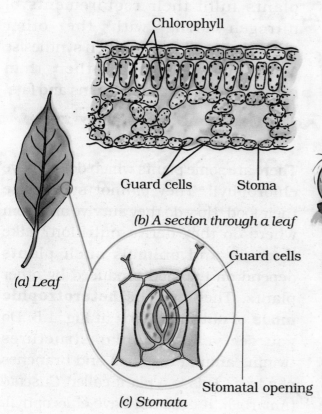

(a) Leaf

Chlorophyll

Guard cells   Stoma

(b) A section through a leaf

Guard cells

Stomatal opening

(c) Stomata

Fig. 1.2

Activity 1.1

Take two potted plants of the same kind. Keep one in the dark (or in a black box) for 72 hours and the other in the sunlight. Perform iodine test with the leaves of both the plants as you did in Class VI. Record your results. Now leave the pot which was earlier kept in the dark, in the sunlight for 3 – 4 days and perform the iodine test again on its leaves. Record your observations in your notebook.

The leaves other than green also have chlorophyll. The large amount of red, brown and other pigments mask the green colour (Fig. 1.4). Photosynthesis takes place in these leaves also.

Fig. 1.4 *Leaves of various colours*

You often see slimy, green patches in ponds or in other stagnant water bodies. These are generally formed by the growth of organisms called **algae**. Can you guess why algae are green in colour? They contain chlorophyll which gives them the green colour. Algae can also prepare their own food by photosynthesis.

Synthesis of plant food other than carbohydrates

You have just learnt that plants synthesise carbohydrates through the process of photosynthesis. The carbohydrates are made of carbon, hydrogen and oxygen. These are used to synthesise other components of food such as proteins and fats. But proteins are nitrogenous substances which contain nitrogen. From where do the plants obtain nitrogen?

Recall that nitrogen is present in abundance in gaseous form in the air. However, plants cannot absorb nitrogen in this form. Soil has certain bacteria that convert gaseous nitrogen into a usable form and release it into the soil. These soluble forms are absorbed by the plants along with water. Also, you might have seen farmers adding fertilisers rich in nitrogen to the soil. In this way the plants fulfil their requirements of nitrogen along with the other constituents. Plants can then synthesise components of food other than carbohydrates such as proteins and fats.

1.3 OTHER MODES OF NUTRITION IN PLANTS

There are some plants which do not have chlorophyll. They cannot synthesise their food. How do they survive and from where do they derive nutrition? Like humans and animals such plants depend on the food produced by other plants. They use the **heterotrophic mode** of nutrition. Look at Fig. 1.5. Do you see yellow tubular structures twining around the stem and branches of a tree? This is a plant called *Cuscuta* (Amarbel). It does not have chlorophyll. It takes readymade food from the plant

Fig. 1.5 *Cuscuta (Amarbel) on host plant*

on which it is climbing. The plant on which it climbs is called a **host**. Since it deprives the host of valuable nutrients, it is called a **parasite**. Are we and the other animals also parasites on the plants? You should think about it and discuss with your teacher.

Paheli wants to know whether mosquitoes, bed bugs, lice and leeches that suck our blood are also parasites.

Have you seen or heard of plants that can eat animals? There are a few plants which can trap insects and digest them. Is it not amazing? Such plants may be green or of some other colour. Look at the plant in Fig. 1.6. The pitcher-like

structure is the modified part of the leaf. The apex of the leaf forms a lid which can open and close the mouth of the pitcher. Inside the pitcher there are hair which are directed downwards. When an insect lands in the pitcher, the lid closes and the trapped insect gets entangled into the hair. The insect is digested by the digestive juices secreted in the pitcher. Such insect-eating plants are called **insectivorous plants**.

Is it possible that such plants do not get all the required nutrients from the soil in which they grow?

Boojho is confused. If the pitcher plant is green and carries out photosynthesis, then why does it feed on insects?

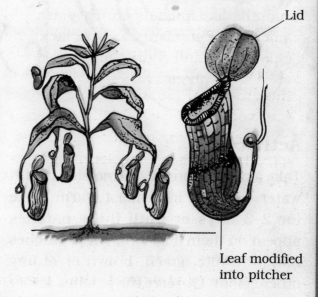

Lid

Leaf modified into pitcher

Fig. 1.6 *Pitcher plant showing lid and pitcher*

1.4 SAPROTROPHS

You might have seen packets of mushrooms sold in the vegetable market. You may have also seen fluffy umbrella-like patches growing on rotting wood during the rainy season (Fig. 1.7). Let us find out what type of nutrients they need to survive and from where they get them.

Fig. 1.7 *Packet of mushrooms, a mushroom growing on decayed material*

Boojho wants to know how these organisms acquire nutrients. They do not have mouths like animals do. They are not like green plants as they lack chlorophyll and cannot make food by photosynthesis.

Activity 1.2

Take a piece of bread and moisten it with water. Leave it in a moist warm place for 2–3 days or until fluffy patches appear on them (Fig. 1.8). These patches may be white, green, brown or of any other colour. Observe the patches under a microscope or a magnifying glass.

Fig. 1.8 *Fungi growing on bread*

Write down your observations in your notebook. Most probably you will see cotton-like threads spread on the piece of bread.

These organisms are called **fungi**. They have a different mode of nutrition. They secrete digestive juices on the dead and decaying matter and convert it into a solution. Then they absorb the nutrients from it. This mode of nutrition in which organisms take in nutrients in solution form from dead and decaying matter is called **saprotrophic nutrition**. Plants which use saprotrophic mode of nutrition are called **saprotrophs**.

Fungi also grow on pickles, leather, clothes and other articles that are left in hot and humid weather for long time.

Paheli is keen to know whether her beautiful shoes, which she wore on special occasions, were spoiled by fungi during the rainy season. She wants to know how fungi appear suddenly during the rainy season.

Boojho says once his grandfather told him that his wheat fields were spoiled by a fungus. He wants to know if fungi cause diseases also.

Paheli told him that many fungi like yeast and mushrooms are useful, but some fungi cause diseases in plants, animals and humans. Some fungi are also used in medicines.

During the rainy season they spoil many things. Ask your parents about the menace of fungi in your house.

The fungal spores are generally present in the air. When they land on wet and warm things they germinate and grow. Now, can you figure out how we can protect our things from getting spoiled?

Some organisms live together and share shelter and nutrients. This is called **symbiotic relationship**. For example, certain fungi live in the roots of trees. The tree provides nutrients to the fungus and, in return, receives help from it to take up water and nutrients from the soil. This association is very important for the tree.

In organisms called **lichens**, a chlorophyll-containing partner, which is an alga, and a fungus live together. The fungus provides shelter, water and minerals to the alga and, in return, the alga provides food which it prepares by photosynthesis.

1.5 HOW NUTRIENTS ARE REPLENISHED IN THE SOIL

Have you seen farmers spreading manure or fertilisers in the fields, or gardeners using them in lawns or in pots? Do you know why they are added to the soil?

You learnt that plants absorb mineral nutrients from the soil. So, their amounts in the soil keep on declining. Fertilisers and manures contain plant nutrients such as nitrogen, potassium, phosphorous, etc. These nutrients need to be added from time to time to enrich the soil. We can grow plants and keep them healthy if we can fulfil the nutrient requirement of plants.

Usually crops require a lot of nitrogen to make proteins. After the harvest, the soil becomes deficient in nitrogen. You learnt that though nitrogen gas is available in plenty in the air, plants cannot use it in the manner they can use carbon dioxide. They need nitrogen in a soluble form. The bacterium called *Rhizobium* can take atmospheric nitrogen and convert it into a soluble form. But *Rhizobium* cannot make its own food. So it lives in the roots of gram, peas, *moong,* beans and other legumes and provides them with nitrogen. Most of the pulses *(dals)* are obtained from leguminous plants. In return, the plants provide food and shelter to the bacteria. They thus have a symbiotic relationship. This association is of great significance for the farmers. They do not need to add nitrogen fertiliser to the soil in which leguminous plants are grown.

In this chapter you learnt that most of the plants are autotrophs. Only a few plants adopt other modes of nutrition like parasitic and saprotrophic. They derive nutrition from other organisms. All animals are categorised as heterotrophs since they depend on plants and other animals for food. Can we say that the insectivorous plants are partial **heterotrophs**?

Keywords

Autotrophic	Insectivorous	Photosynthesis
Chlorophyll	Nutrient	Saprotrophs
Heterotrophs	Nutrition	Saprotrophic
Host	Parasite	Stomata

What you have learnt

- All organisms take food and utilise it to get energy for the growth and maintenance of their bodies.
- Green plants synthesise their food themselves by the process of photosynthesis. They are autotrophs.
- Plants use simple chemical substances like carbon dioxide, water and minerals for the synthesis of food.
- Chlorophyll and sunlight are the essential requirements for photosynthesis.
- Complex chemical substances such as carbohydrates are the products of photosynthesis.
- Solar energy is stored in the form of food in the leaves with the help of chlorophyll.
- Oxygen is produced during photosynthesis.
- Oxygen released in photosynthesis is utilised by living organisms for their survival.
- Fungi derive nutrition from dead, decaying matter. They are saprotrophs. Plants like *Cuscuta* are parasites. They take food from the host plant.
- A few plants and all animals are dependent on others for their nutrition and are called heterotrophs.

Exercise

1. Why do organisms need to take food?

2. Distinguish between a parasite and a saprotroph.

3. How would you test the presence of starch in leaves?

4. Give a brief description of the process of synthesis of food in green plants.

5. Show with the help of a sketch that the plants are the ultimate source of food.

6. Fill in the blanks:

   (a) Green plants are called _____ since they synthesise their own food.

   (b) The food synthesised by the plants is stored as _____.

   (c) In photosynthesis solar energy is captured by the pigment called _____.

   (d) During photosynthesis plants take in _____ and release _____.

7. Name the following:

   (i) A parasitic plant with yellow, slender and tubular stem.

   (ii) A plant that has both autotrophic and heterotrophic mode of nutrition.

   (iii) The pores through which leaves exchange gases.

8. Tick the correct answer:

   (a) *Amarbel* is an example of:

   (i) autotroph (ii) parasite (iii) saprotroph (iv) host

   (b) The plant which traps and feeds on insects is:

   (i) *Cuscuta* (ii) china rose (iv) pitcher plant (iv) rose

9. Match the items given in Column I with those in Column II:

Column I	Column II
Chlorophyll	Bacteria
Nitrogen	Heterotrophs
Amarbel	Pitcher plant
Animals	Leaf
Insects	Parasite

10. Mark 'T' if the statement is true and 'F' if it is false:

   (i) Carbon dioxide is released during photosynthesis. (T/F)

(ii) Plants which synthesise their food themselves are called saprotrophs. (T/F)

(iii) The product of photosynthesis is not a protein. (T/F)

(iv) Solar energy is converted into chemical energy during photosynthesis. (T/F)

11. Choose the correct option from the following:

Which part of the plant takes in carbon dioxide from the air for photosynthesis?

(i) Root hair (ii) Stomata (iii) Leaf veins (iv) Sepals

12. Choose the correct option from the following:

Plants take carbon dioxide from the atmosphere mainly through their:

(i) roots (ii) stem (iii) flowers (iv) leaves

Extended Learning — Activities and Projects

1. Project

Take a potted plant with broad leaves. Take two strips of black paper and cut out a small square in their centres. Cover a part of two leaves with these papers and secure them with paper clips (Fig. 1.9). Keep the plant in the sunlight for 2–5 days. Observe the difference in the colour of the covered and the uncovered portions on the one leaf. Perform iodine test on this leaf. Did the two parts show any difference in results? Now take second leaf. Remove the strip and expose the covered part to the sunlight for 2–3 days and do the iodine test again. Describe your observations.

Fig. 1.9 *Experiment to test the occurrence of photosynthesis*

2. Visit a green house if there is one near your place. Observe how they raise plants. Find out how they regulate the amount of light, water and carbon dioxide to grow the plants.

3. Try growing a sweet potato just in water. Describe your experiment and observations.

You can read more on the following website:

www.phschool.com/science/biology_place/biocoach/photosynth/overview.htm

Did you know?

Light is so important to plants that their leaves grow in many patterns so as to catch the most sunlight.

2 Nutrition in Animals

You have learnt in Chapter 1 that plants can prepare their own food by the process of photosynthesis but animals cannot. Animals get their food from plants, either directly by eating plants or indirectly by eating animals that eat plants. Some animals eat both plants and animals. Recall that all organisms including humans require food for growth, repair and functioning of the body. **Animal nutrition includes nutrient requirement, mode of intake of food and its utilisation in the body.**

You have studied in Class VI that food consists of many components. Try to recall and list them below:

1. _____
2. _____
3. _____
4. _____
5. _____
6. _____

The components of food such as carbohydrates are complex substances. These complex substances cannot be utilised as such. So they are broken down into simpler substances. The breakdown of complex components of

Complex substance   Simpler substances

food into simpler substances is called **digestion**.

2.1 DIFFERENT WAYS OF TAKING FOOD

The mode of taking food into the body varies in different organisms. Bees and humming-birds suck the nectar of plants, infants of human and many other animals feed on mother's milk. Snakes like the python swallow the animals they prey upon. Some aquatic animals filter tiny food particles floating nearby and feed upon them.

Activity 2.1

What is the type of food and mode of feeding of the following animals? Write down your observations in the given Table. You may find the list of modes of feeding given below the Table helpful.

Table 2.1 Various modes of feeding

Name of animal	Kind of food	Mode of feeding
Snail		
Ant		
Eagle		
Humming-bird		
Lice		
Mosquito		
Butterfly		
House fly		

(Scraping, chewing, siphoning, capturing and swallowing, sponging sucking etc.)

Starfish feeds on animals covered by hard shells of calcium carbonate. After opening the shell, the starfish pops out its stomach through its mouth to eat the soft animal inside the shell. The stomach then goes back into the body and the food is slowly digested.

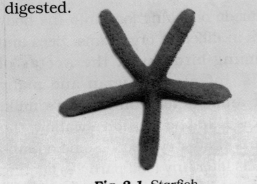

***Fig. 2.1** Starfish*

2.2 Digestion in Humans

We take in food through the mouth, digest and utilise it. The unused parts of the food are defecated. Have you ever wondered what happens to the food inside the body? The food passes through a continuous canal (Fig. 2.2) which begins at the buccal cavity and ends at the anus. The canal can be divided into various compartments: (1) the **buccal cavity,** (2) foodpipe or **oesophagus**, (3) **stomach**, (4) **small intestine**, (5) **large intestine** ending in the **rectum** and (6) the **anus**. Is it not a very long path? These parts together form the **alimentary canal (digestive tract)**. The food components gradually get digested as food travels through the various compartments. The inner walls of the stomach and the small intestine, and the various glands associated with the canal such as **salivary glands**, the **liver** and the **pancreas** secrete digestive juices. The digestive juices convert complex

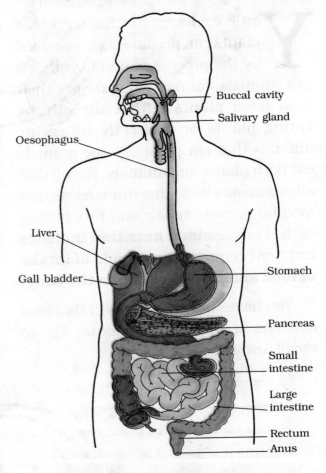

***Fig. 2.2** Human digestive system*

substances of food into simpler ones. The digestive tract and the associated glands together constitute the **digestive system**.

Now, let us know what happens to the food in different parts of the digestive tract.

The mouth and buccal cavity

Food is taken into the body through the mouth. The process of taking food into

Milk teeth and permanent teeth

Do you remember about falling of your teeth some years ago? The first set of teeth grows during infancy and they fall off at the age between six to eight years. These are termed **milk teeth**. The second set that replaces them are the **permanent teeth**. The permanent teeth may last throughout life or fall off during old age or due to some dental disease.

Boojho is fascinated by the highly coiled small intestine seen in Fig. 2.2. He wants to know its length. Would you like to make a wild guess? We have given its approximate length on page 16. Just imagine how such a long structure is accommodated in a small space within our body!

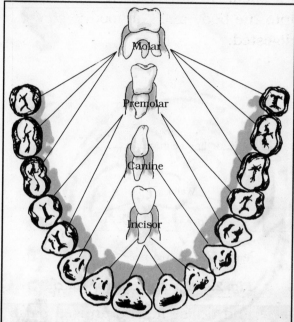

Fig. 2.3 *Arrangement of teeth and different type of teeth*

the body is called **ingestion**. We chew the food with the teeth and break it down mechanically into small pieces. Each tooth is rooted in a separate socket in the gums (Fig. 2.3). Our teeth vary in appearance and perform different functions. Accordingly they are given different names (Fig. 2.3).

Activity 2.2

Wash your hands. Look into the mirror and count your teeth. Use your index finger to feel the teeth. How many kinds of teeth could you find? Take a piece of an apple or bread and eat it. Which teeth do you use for biting and cutting, and which ones for piercing and tearing? Also find out the ones that are used for chewing and grinding?

Record your observations in Table 2.2

Table 2.2

Type of teeth	Number of teeth		Total
	Lower jaw	Upper jaw	
Cutting and biting teeth			
Piercing and tearing teeth			
Chewing and grinding teeth			

Our mouth has the salivary glands which secrete saliva. Do you know the action of saliva on food? Let us find out.

Activity 2.3

Take two test tubes. Label them 'A' and 'B'. In test tube 'A' put one teaspoonful of boiled rice; in test tube 'B' keep one teaspoonful of boiled rice after chewing it for 3 to 5 minutes. Add 3–4 mL of water in both the test tubes (Fig. 2.4). Now pour 2–3 drops of iodine solution in each test tube and observe. Why is there a change in colour in the test tubes? Discuss the results with your classmates and your teacher. The **saliva** breaks down the **starch** into sugars.

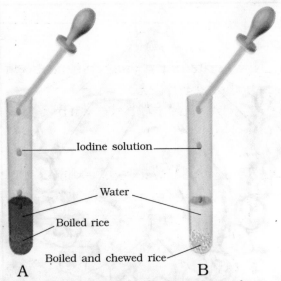

Fig. 2.4 *Effect of saliva on starch*

Labels: Iodine solution, Water, Boiled rice, Boiled and chewed rice, A, B

The tongue is a fleshy muscular organ attached at the back to the floor of the buccal cavity. It is free at the front and can be moved in all directions. Do you know the functions of the tongue? We use our tongue for talking. Besides, it mixes saliva with the food during chewing and helps in swallowing food. We also taste food with our tongue. It has taste buds that detect different tastes of food. We can find out the

Sweets and tooth decay

Normally bacteria are present in our mouth but they are not harmful to us. However, if we do not clean our teeth and mouth after eating, many harmful bacteria also begin to live and grow in it. These bacteria break down the sugars present from the leftover food and release acids (see Chapter 5 to know what an acid is). The acids gradually damage the teeth (Fig. 2.5). This is called **tooth decay**. If it is not treated in time, it causes severe toothache and in extreme cases results in tooth loss. Chocolates, sweets, soft drinks and other sugar products are the major culprits of tooth decay.

Therefore, one should clean the teeth with a brush or *datun* and dental floss (a special strong thread which is moved between two teeth to take out trapped food particles) at least twice a day and rinse the mouth after every meal. Also, one should not put dirty fingers or any unwashed object in the mouth.

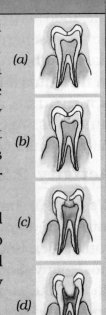

(a)
(b)
(c)
(d)

Fig. 2.5 *Gradual decay of tooth*

Sometimes when you eat in a hurry, talk or laugh while eating, you may cough, get hiccups or a choking sensation. This happens when food particles enter the windpipe. The windpipe carries air from the nostrils to the lungs. It runs adjacent to the foodpipe. But inside the throat, air and food share a common passage. Then how is food prevented from entering the windpipe? During the act of swallowing a flap-like valve closes the passage of the windpipe and guides the food into the foodpipe. If, by chance, food particles enter the windpipe, we feel choked, get hiccups or cough.

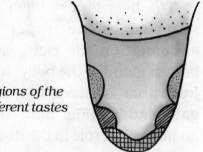

Fig. 2.6 *Regions of the tongue for different tastes*

position of taste buds by the following activity.

Activity 2.4

1. Prepare a separate sample each of (i) sugar solution, (ii) common salt solution, (iii) lemon juice and (iv) juice of crushed neem leaf or bitter gourd.
2. Blindfold one of your classmates and ask her/him to take out the tongue and keep it in straight and flat position.
3. Use a clean toothpick to put the above samples one by one on different areas of the tongue as shown in Fig. 2.6. Use a new toothpick for each sample.
4. Ask the classmate which areas of the tongue could detect the sweet, salty, sour and bitter substances.

5. Now write down your observations and label Fig. 2.6.

Repeat this activity with other classmates.

The foodpipe/oesophagus

The swallowed food passes into the foodpipe or oesophagus. Look at Fig. 2.2. The foodpipe runs along the neck

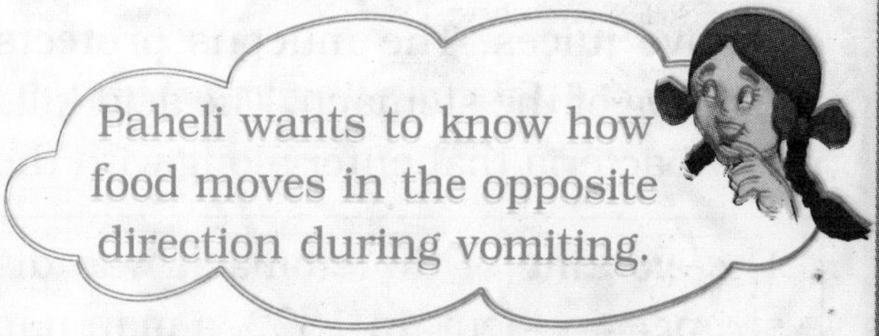

Paheli wants to know how food moves in the opposite direction during vomiting.

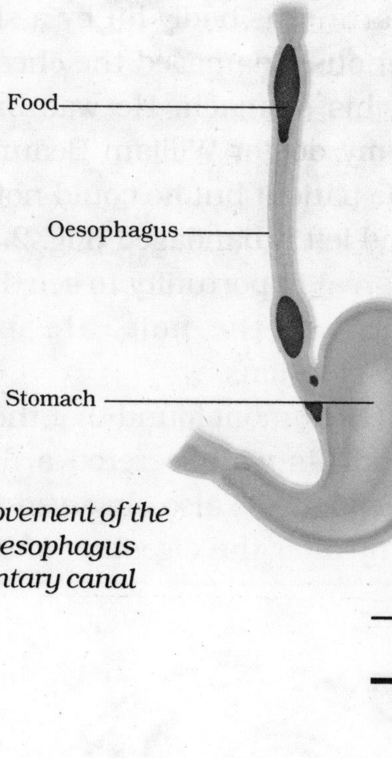

Food——

Oesophagus ——

Stomach ——

Fig. 2.7 *Movement of the food in the oesophagus of the alimentary canal*

and the chest. Food is pushed down by movement of the wall of the foodpipe. Actually this movement takes place throughout the alimentary canal and pushes the food downwards (Fig. 2.7). At times the food is not accepted by our stomach and is vomited out. Recall the instances when you vomited after eating and think of the reason for it. Discuss with your parents and teacher.

The stomach

The stomach is a thick-walled bag. Its shape is like a flattened U and it is the widest part of the alimentary canal. It receives food from the food pipe at one end and opens into the small intestine at the other.

The inner lining of the stomach secretes mucous, hydrochloric acid and digestive juices. The mucous protects the lining of the stomach. The acid kills many bacteria that enter along with the food and makes the medium in the stomach acidic and helps the digestive juices to act. The digestive juices break down the **proteins** into simpler substances.

The small intestine

The small intestine is highly coiled and is about 7.5 metres long. It receives secretions from the liver and the pancreas. Besides, its wall also secretes juices.

The liver is a reddish brown gland situated in the upper part of the abdomen on the right side. It is the largest gland in the body. It secretes **bile juice** that is stored in a sac called the **gall bladder** (Fig. 2.2). The bile plays an important role in the digestion of **fats**.

The pancreas is a large cream coloured gland located just below the stomach (Fig. 2.2). The pancreatic juice acts on carbohydrates, fats and proteins and changes them into simpler forms.

The working of the stomach was discovered by a strange accident. In 1822, a man named Alexis St. Martin was badly hit by a shot gun. The bullet had seriously damaged the chest wall and made a hole in his stomach. He was brought to an American army doctor William Beaumont. The doctor saved the patient but he could not close the hole properly and left it bandaged (Fig. 2.8). Beaumont took it as a great opportunity to see the inside of the stomach through the hole. He made some wonderful observations.

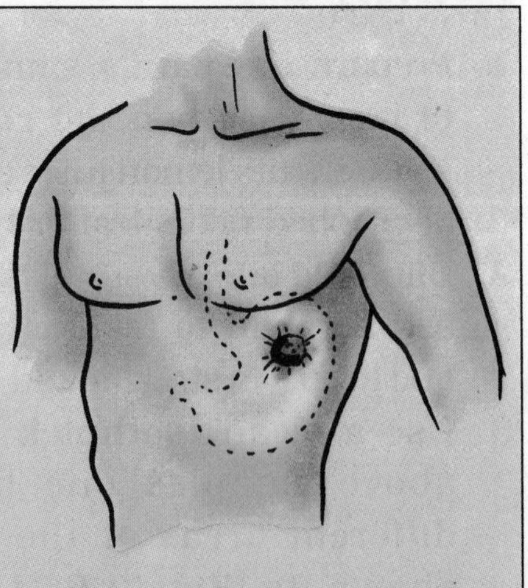

Beaumont found that the stomach was churning food. Its wall secreted a fluid which could digest the food. He also observed that the end of the stomach opens into the intestine only after the digestion of the food inside the stomach is completed.

Fig. 2.8 Alexis St. Martin's shotgun wound

The partly digested food now reaches the lower part of the small intestine where the intestinal juice completes the digestion of all components of the food. The carbohydrates get broken into simple sugars such as glucose, fats into fatty acids and glycerol, and proteins into amino acids.

Absorption in the small intestine

The digested food can now pass into the blood vessels in the wall of the intestine. This process is called **absorption**. The inner walls of the small intestine have thousands of finger-like outgrowths. These are called **villi** (singular villus). Can you guess what the role of villi could be in the intestine? The villi increase the surface area for absorption of the digested food. Each villus has a network of thin and small blood vessels close to its surface. The surface of the villi absorbs the digested food materials. The absorbed substances are transported via the blood vessels to different organs of the body where they are used to build complex substances such as the proteins required by the body. This is called **assimilation**. In the cells, glucose breaks down with the help of oxygen into carbon dioxide and water, and energy is released. The food that remains undigested and unabsorbed enters into the large intestine.

Large intestine

The large intestine is wider and shorter than small intestine. It is about 1.5 metre in length. Its function is to absorb water and some salts from the undigested food material. The remaining waste passes into the rectum and remains there as semi-solid faeces. The faecal matter is removed through the anus from time-to-time. This is called **egestion**.

2.3 DIGESTION IN GRASS-EATING ANIMALS

Have you observed cows, buffaloes and other grass-eating animals chewing continuously even when they are not eating? Actually, they quickly swallow the grass and store it in a part of the stomach called **rumen** (Fig. 2.9). Here the food gets

---

Diarrhoea

Sometime you may have experienced the need to pass watery stool frequently. This condition is known as **diarrhoea**. It may be caused by an infection, food poisoning or indigestion. It is very common in India, particularly among children. Under severe conditions it can be fatal. This is because of the excessive loss of water and salts from the body. Diarrhoea should not be neglected. Even before a doctor is consulted the patient should be given plenty of boiled and cooled water with a pinch of salt and sugar dissolved in it. This is called **Oral Rehydration Solution** (**ORS**).

Paheli wants to know why these animals cannot chew food properly at the time they take it in?

Boojho wants to know why we cannot digest cellulose like the cattle do.

partially digested and is called **cud**. But later the cud returns to the mouth in small lumps and the animal chews it. This process is called **rumination** and these animals are called **ruminants**.

The grass is rich in **cellulose**, a type of carbohydrate. Many animals, including humans, cannot digest cellulose.

Ruminants have a large sac-like structure called Caecum between the small intestine and large intestine (Fig. 2.9). The cellulose of the food is digested here by the action of certain bacteria which are not present in humans.

So far you have learnt about animals which possess the digestive system. But there are many small organisms which do not have a mouth and a digestive system. Then, how do they acquire and digest food? In the section below you will learn another interesting way of food intake.

2.4 FEEDING AND DIGESTION IN AMOEBA

Amoeba is a microscopic single-celled organism found in pond water. Amoeba has a cell membrane, a rounded, dense nucleus and many small bubble-like vacuoles (Fig. 2.10) in its cytoplasm. Amoeba constantly changes its shape and position. It pushes out one, or more finger-like projections, called **pseudopodia** or false feet for movement and capture of food.

Amoeba feeds on some microscopic organisms. When it senses food, it

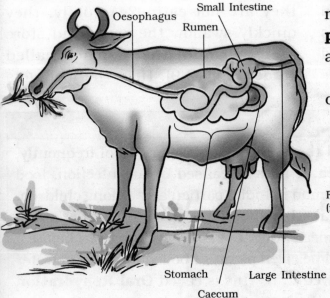

Fig. 2.9 *Digestive system of ruminant*

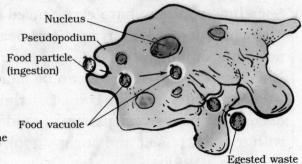

Fig. 2.10 *Amoeba*

pushes out pseudopodia around the food particle and engulfs it. The food becomes trapped in a **food vacuole** [Fig. 2.10).

Digestive juices are secreted into the food vacuole. They act on the food and break it down into simpler substances. Gradually the digested food is absorbed. The absorbed substances are used for growth, maintenance and multiplication. The undigested residue of the food is expelled outside by the vacuole.

The basic process of digestion of food and release of energy is the same in all animals. In a later chapter you will learn about the transport of food absorbed by the intestine to the various parts of the body.

Keywords

Absorption	Fatty acid	Oesophagus
Amino acid	Food vacuole	Pancreas
Amoeba	Gall bladder	Premolar
Assimilation	Glycerol	Pseudopodia
Bile	Incisor	Rumen
Buccal cavity	Ingestion	Ruminant
Canine	Liver	Rumination
Cellulose	Milk teeth	Salivary glands
Digestion	Molar	Villi
Egestion	Permanent teeth	Saliva

What you have learnt

- Animal nutrition includes nutrient requirement, mode of intake of food and its utilisation in the body.

- The human digestive system consists of the alimentary canal and secretory glands. It consists of the (i) buccal cavity, (ii) oesophagus, (iii) stomach, (iv) small intestine, (v) large intestine ending in rectum and (vi) anus. The main digestive glands which secrete digestive juices are (i) the salivary glands, (ii) the liver and (iii) the pancreas. The stomach wall and the wall of the small intestine also secrete digestive juices.

- The modes of feeding vary in different organisms.

- Nutrition is a complex process involving: (i) ingestion, (ii) digestion, (iii) absorption, (iv) assimilation and (v) egestion.

- Digestion of carbohydrates, like starch, begins in the buccal cavity. The digestion of protein starts in the stomach. The bile secreted from the liver, the pancreatic juice from the pancreas and the digestive juice from the intestinal wall complete the digestion of all components of food in the small intestine. The digested food is absorbed in the blood vessels from the small intestine.

- The absorbed substances are transported to different parts of the body. Water and some salts are absorbed from the undigested food in the large intestine.

- The undigested and unabsorbed residues are expelled out of the body as faeces through the anus.

- The grazing animals like cows, buffaloes and deer are known as ruminants. They quickly ingest, swallow their leafy food and store it in the rumen. Later, the food returns to the mouth and the animal chews it peacefully.

- Amoeba ingests its food with the help of its false feet or pseudopodia. The food is digested in the food vacuole.

Exercises

1. Fill in the blanks:

   (a) The main steps of nutrition in humans are _____, _____, _____, _____ and _____.

   (b) The largest gland in the human body is _____.

   (c) The stomach releases hydrochloric acid and _____ juices which act on food.

   (d) The inner wall of the small intestine has many finger-like outgrowths called _____.

   (e) Amoeba digests its food in the _____.

2. Mark 'T' if the statement is true and 'F' if it is false:

   (a) Digestion of starch starts in the stomach. (T/F)

   (b) The tongue helps in mixing food with saliva. (T/F)

   (c) The gall bladder temporarily stores bile. (T/F)

   (d) The ruminants bring back swallowed grass into their mouth and chew it for some time. (T/F)

3. Tick (✓) mark the correct answer in each of the following:

   (a) Fat is completely digested in the

   (i) stomach (ii) mouth (iii) small intestine (iv) large intestine

(b) Water from the undigested food is absorbed mainly in the

  (i) stomach (ii) foodpipe (iii) small intestine (iv) large intestine

4. Match the items of Column I with those given in Column II:

Column I	Column II
Food components	Product(s) of digestion
Carbohydrates	Fatty acids and glycerol
Proteins	Sugar
Fats	Amino acids

5. What are villi? What is their location and function?

6. Where is the bile produced? Which component of the food does it help to digest?

7. Name the type of carbohydrate that can be digested by ruminants but not by humans. Give the reason also.

8. Why do we get instant energy from glucose?

9. Which part of the digestive canal is involved in:

  (i) absorption of food _____.

  (ii) chewing of food _____.

  (iii) killing of bacteria _____.

  (iv) complete digestion of food _____.

  (v) formation of faeces _____.

10. Write one similarity and one difference between the nutrition in amoeba and human beings.

11. Match the items of Column I with suitable items in Column II

Column I	Column II
(a) Salivary gland	(i) Bile juice secretion
(b) Stomach	(ii) Storage of undigested food
(c) Liver	(iii) Saliva secretion
(d) Rectum	(iv) Acid release
(e) Small intestine	(v) Digestion is completed
(f) Large intestine	(vi) Absorption of water
	(vii) Release of faeces

12. Label Fig. 2.11 of the digestive system.

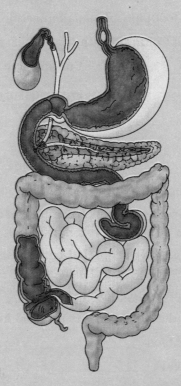

Fig. 2.11 *A part of human digestive system*

13. Can we survive only on raw, leafy vegetables/grass? Discuss.

Extended Learning — Activities and Project

1. Visit a doctor and find out:

   (i)   Under what conditions does a patient need to be on a drip of glucose?

   (ii) Till when does a patient need to be given glucose?

   (iii) How does glucose help the patient recover?

   Write the answers in your notebook.

2. Find out what vitamins are and get the following information.

   (i)   Why are vitamins necessary in the diet?

   (ii) Which fruits or vegetables should be eaten regularly to get vitamins?

   Write a one-page note on the information collected by you. You may take help of a doctor, a dietician, your teacher or any other person, or from any other source.

3. Collect data from your friends, neighbours and classmates to know more about "milk teeth".

Tabulate your data. One way of doing it is given below:

S. No.	Age at which first tooth fell	Age at which last tooth fell	No. of teeth lost	No. of teeth replaced
1.				
2.				
3.				
4.				
5.				

Find out from at least twenty children and find the average age at which children lose the milk teeth. You may take help of your friends.

You can read more on the following website:

www.health.howstuffworks.com/adam-200142.htm

Did you know?

Fats in goat's milk are much simpler than those in cow's milk. Therefore, the goat's milk is much easier to digest than the cow's milk.

3 Fibre to Fabric

In Class VI you have learnt about some fibres obtained from plants. You also learnt that wool and silk fibres are obtained from animals. Wool is obtained from the **fleece** (hair) of sheep or yak. Silk fibres come from cocoons of the silk moth. Do you know which part of the sheep's body yields fibres? Are you aware how these fibres are converted into the woollen yarn that we buy from the market to knit sweaters? Do you have any idea how silk fibres are made into silk, which is woven into saris?

In this Chapter we shall try to find answers to these questions.

Animal fibres — wool and silk

3.1 Wool

Wool comes from sheep, goat, yak and some other animals. These wool-yielding animals bear hair on their body. Do you know why these animals have a thick coat of hair? Hair trap a lot of air. Air is a poor conductor of heat, as you would learn in Chapter 4. So, hair keeps these animals warm. Wool is derived from these hairy fibres.

Activity 3.1

Feel the hair on your body and arms and those on your head. Do you find any difference? Which one seems coarse and which one is soft?

Like us, the hairy skin of the sheep has two types of fibres that form its fleece: (i) the coarse beard hair, and (ii) the fine soft under-hair close to the skin. The fine hair provide the fibres for making wool. Some breeds of sheep possess only fine under-hair. Their parents are specially chosen to give birth to sheep which have only soft under-hair. This process of selecting parents for obtaining special characters in their offspring, such as soft under hair in sheep, is termed 'selective breeding'.

Fig. 3.1 *Sheep with thick growth of hair*

Animals that yield wool

Several breeds of sheep are found in different parts of our country (Table 3.1). However, the fleece of sheep is not the only source of wool, though wool commonly available in the market is sheep wool (Fig. 3.1). Yak (Fig. 3.2) wool is common in Tibet and Ladakh. Angora wool is obtained from angora goats, (Fig. 3.3) found in hilly regions such as Jammu and Kashmir.

Wool is also obtained from goat hair (Fig. 3.4). The under fur of Kashmiri goat is soft. It is woven into fine shawls called Pashmina shawls.

The fur (hair) on the body of camels is also used as wool (Fig. 3.5). Llama and Alpaca, found in South America, also yield wool (Fig. 3.6 and 3.7).

Activity 3.2

Collect pictures of animals whose hair is used as wool. Stick them in your scrap book. If you are unable to get pictures, try and draw them from the ones given in this book.

Find out words for sheep, goat, camel and yak in your local language and also in other languages of our country.

Fig. 3.2 Yak

Fig. 3.6 Llama

Activity 3.3

Procure outline maps of India and the world. Find out and mark the places on the map where you find animals that provide wool. Use different colours to denote the location for different wool yielding animals.

Fig. 3.3 Angora goat   **Fig. 3.4** Goat

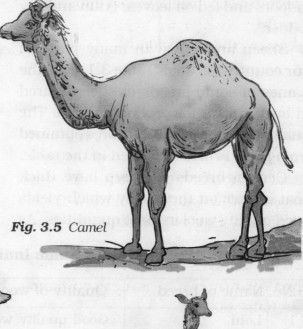

Fig. 3.5 Camel

Fig. 3.7 Alpaca

From fibres to wool

For obtaining wool, sheep are reared. Their hair is cut and processed into wool. Let us learn about this process.

Rearing and breeding of sheep: If you travel to the hills in Jammu & Kashmir, Himachal Pradesh, Uttaranchal, Arunachal Pradesh and Sikkim, or the plains of Haryana, Punjab, Rajasthan and Gujarat, you can see shepherds taking their herds of sheep for grazing. Sheep are herbivores and prefer grass and leaves. Apart from grazing sheep, rearers also feed them on a mixture of pulses, corn, jowar, oil cakes (material left after taking out oil from seeds) and minerals. In winter, sheep are kept indoors and fed on leaves, grain and dry fodder.

Sheep are reared in many parts of our country for wool. Table 3.1 gives the names of some breeds of sheep reared in our country for producing wool. The quality and texture of the fibres obtained from them is also indicated in the table.

Certain breeds of sheep have thick coat of hair on their body which yields good quality wool in large quantities. As mentioned earlier, these sheep are "selectively bred" with one parent being a sheep of good breed.

Once the reared sheep have developed a thick growth of hair, hair is shaved off for getting wool.

Processing fibres into wool

The wool which is used for knitting sweaters or for weaving shawls is the finished product of a long process, which involves the following steps:

Step I: The fleece of the sheep along with a thin layer of skin is removed from its body [Fig. 3.8 (a)]. This process is called **shearing**. Machines similar to those used by barbers are used to shave off hair. Usually, hair are removed during the hot weather. This enables sheep to survive without their protective coat of hair. The hair provide woollen fibres. Woollen fibres are then processed to obtain woollen yarn. Shearing does not hurt the sheep just as it does not hurt when you get a hair cut or your father shaves his beard. Do you know why? The uppermost layer of the skin is dead. Also, the hair of sheep grow again just as your hair does.

Table 3.1 Some Indian breeds of sheep

S.No.	Name of breed	Quality of wool	State where found
1.	Lohi	Good quality wool	Rajasthan, Punjab
2.	Rampur bushair	Brown fleece	Uttar Pradesh, Himachal Pradesh
3.	Nali	Carpet wool	Rajasthan, Haryana, Punjab
4.	Bakharwal	For woollen shawls	Jammu and Kashmir
5.	Marwari	Coarse wool	Gujarat
6.	Patanwadi	For hosiery	Gujarat

Step II: The sheared skin with hair is thoroughly washed in tanks to remove grease, dust and dirt. This is called **scouring**. Nowadays scouring is done by machines [Fig. 3.8 (b) and (c)].

Step III: After scouring, **sorting** is done. The hairy skin is sent to a factory where hair of different textures are separated or sorted.

Step IV: The small fluffy fibres, called burrs, are picked out from the hair. These are the same burrs which

sometimes appear on your sweaters. The fibres are scoured again and dried. This is the wool ready to be drawn into fibres.

Step V: The fibres can be dyed in various colours, as the natural fleece of sheep and goats is black, brown or white.

Step VI: The fibres are straightened, combed and rolled into yarn [Fig. 3.8 (d)]. The longer fibres are made into wool for sweaters and the shorter fibres are spun and woven into woollen cloth.

Fig. 3.8 (a) Shearing a sheep

Fig. 3.8 (b) Scouring in tanks

Fig. 3.8 (c) Scouring by machines

Fig. 3.8 (d) Rolling into yarn

Occupational hazard

Wool industry is an important means of livelihood for many people in our country. But sorter's job is risky as sometimes they get infected by a bacterium, *anthrax*, which causes a fatal blood disease called sorter's disease. Such risks faced by workers in any industry are called occupational hazards.

Boojho is wondering why it hurts when someone pulls his hair but not when he goes for a haircut.

Boojho is wondering why a cotton garment cannot keep us as warm in winter as a woollen sweater does.

Activity 3.4

Debate amongst your classmates whether it is fair on the part of humans to rear sheep and then chop off their hair for getting wool.

3.2 SILK

Silk fibres are also animal fibres. Silkworms spin the 'silk fibres'. The rearing of silkworms for obtaining silk is called **sericulture**. Find out from your mother/aunt/grandmother the kind of silk saris they have. List the kinds of silk.

Before we discuss the process of obtaining silk, it is necessary to know the interesting life history of the silk moth.

Life history of silk moth

The female silk moth lays eggs, from which hatch larvae which are called **caterpillars** or **silkworms**. They grow in size and when the caterpillar is ready to enter the next stage of its life history called **pupa**, it first weaves a net to hold itself. Then it swings its head from side to side in the form of the figure of eight (8). During these movements of the head, the caterpillar secretes fibre made of a

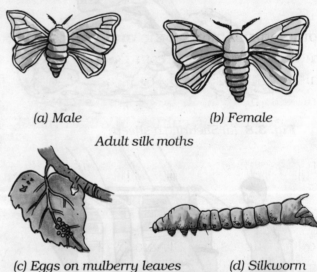

(a) Male (b) Female

Adult silk moths

(c) Eggs on mulberry leaves (d) Silkworm

(e) Cocoon (f) Cocoon with developing moth

Fig. 3.9 *(a to f) Life history of silk moth*

protein which hardens on exposure to air and becomes silk fibre. Soon the caterpillar completely covers itself by silk fibres and turns into pupa. This covering is known as **cocoon**. The further development of the pupa into moth continues inside the cocoon (Fig. 3.9). Silk fibres are used for weaving silk cloth. Can you imagine that the soft silk yarn is as strong as a comparable thread of steel!

The silk yarn (thread) is obtained from the cocoon of the silk moth. There is a variety of silk moths which look very different from one another and the silk yarn they yield is different in texture (coarse, smooth, shiny, etc.). Thus, *tassar* silk, *mooga* silk, *kosa* silk, etc., are obtained from cocoons spun by different types of moths. The most common silk moth is the **mulberry silk moth**. The silk fibre from the cocoon of this moth is soft, lustrous and elastic and can be dyed in beautiful colours.

Sericulture or culture of silkworms is a very old occupation in India. India produces plenty of silk on a commercial scale.

Activity 3.5

Collect pieces of silk cloth of various types and paste them in your scrap book. You can find them in a tailor's shop among the heap of waste cut pieces.

Take help of your mother, aunt or teacher and identify the types of silk such as mulberry silk, *tassar* silk, *eri* silk, *mooga* silk, etc. Compare the texture of these silks with that of the artificial silk pieces, which contain synthetic fibres. Try and collect pictures of different moths whose caterpillars provide the various types of silk.

Activity 3.6

Take an artificial (synthetic) silk thread and a pure silk thread. Burn these threads carefully. Did you notice any difference in the smell while burning? Now, burn a woollen fibre carefully. Did it smell like burning of artificial silk or that of pure silk? Can you explain why?

To remember when the cocoon stage is reached in the life history of the silk moth, try the following activity.

Activity 3.7

Photocopy Fig. 3.9. Cut out pictures of the stages of the life history of the silk moth, and paste them on pieces of cardboard or chart paper. Jumble them. Now try and arrange the stages in the correct sequence in a cyclic form. Whoever does it fastest wins.

You may also describe the life history in your own words. Write it down in your scrap book.

In India, women are significantly involved in various kinds of industries related to silk production. These are rearing of silkworms, reeling of silk from cocoons and processing of raw silk into fabrics. By their enterprise, they contribute to the nation's economy. China leads the world in silk production. India also ranks among the leading silk producing countries.

From cocoon to silk

For obtaining silk, moths are reared and their cocoons are collected to get silk threads.

Rearing silkworms: A female silk moth lays hundreds of eggs at a time [Fig. 3.10 (a)]. The eggs are stored carefully on strips of cloth or paper and sold to silkworm farmers. The farmers keep eggs under hygienic conditions and under suitable conditions of temperature and humidity.

The eggs are warmed to a suitable temperature for the larvae to hatch from eggs. This is done when mulberry trees [Fig. 3.10 (b)] bear a fresh crop of leaves. The larvae, called caterpillars or silkworms, eat day and night and increase enormously in size [Fig. 3.10 (c)].

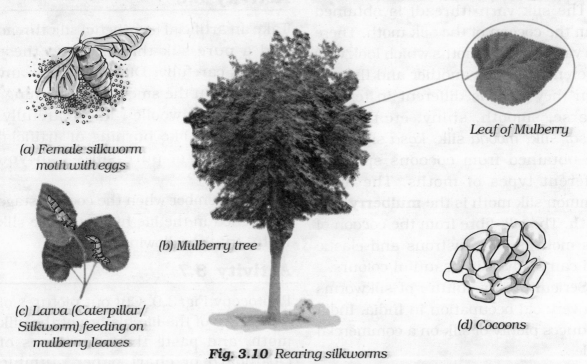

(a) Female silkworm moth with eggs

Leaf of Mulberry

(b) Mulberry tree

(c) Larva (Caterpillar/ Silkworm) feeding on mulberry leaves

(d) Cocoons

Fig. 3.10 Rearing silkworms

Discovery of silk

The exact time of discovery of silk is perhaps unknown. According to an old Chinese legend, the empress Si-lung-Chi was asked by the emperor Huang-ti to find the cause of the damaged leaves of mulberry trees growing in their garden. The empress found white worms eating up mulberry leaves. She also noticed that they were spinning shiny cocoons around them. Accidentally a cocoon dropped into her cup of tea and a tangle of delicate threads separated from the cocoon. Silk industry began in China and was kept a closely guarded secret for hundreds of years. Later on, traders and travellers introduced silk to other countries. The route they travelled is still called the 'silk route'.

The larvae are kept in clean bamboo trays along with freshly chopped mulberry leaves. After 25 to 30 days, the caterpillars stop eating and move to a tiny chamber of bamboo in the tray to spin cocoons [Fig. 3.10 (d)]. Small racks or twigs may be provided in the trays to which cocoons get attached. The caterpillar or silkworm spins the cocoon inside which develops the silk moth.

Processing silk: A pile of cocoons is used for obtaining silk fibres. The cocoons are kept under the sun or boiled or exposed to steam. The silk fibres

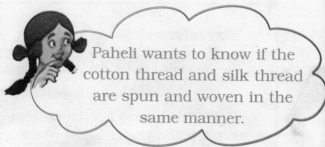
Paheli wants to know if the cotton thread and silk thread are spun and woven in the same manner.

separate out. The process of taking out threads from the cocoon for use as silk is called **reeling the silk**. Reeling is done in special machines, which unwind the threads or fibres of silk from the cocoon. Silk fibres are then spun into silk threads, which are woven into silk cloth by weavers.

Keywords

Cocoon	Scouring	Silk moth
Fleece	Sericulture	Silkworm
Reeling	Shearing	Sorting

What you have learnt

- Silk comes from silkworms and wool is obtained from sheep, goat and yak. Hence silk and wool are animal fibres.

- The hairs of camel, llama and alpaca are also processed to yield wool.

- In India, mostly sheep are reared for getting wool.

- Sheep hair is sheared off from the body, scoured, sorted, dried, dyed, spun and woven to yield wool.

- Silkworms are caterpillars of silk moth.

- During their life cycle, the worms spin cocoons of silk fibres.

- Silk fibres are made of a protein.

- Silk fibres from cocoons are separated out and reeled into silk threads.

- Weavers weave silk threads into silk cloth.

Exercises

1. You must be familiar with the following nursery rhymes:

   (i) 'Baa baa black sheep, have you any wool.'

   (ii) 'Mary had a little lamb, whose fleece was white as snow.'

   Answer the following:

   (a) Which parts of the black sheep have wool?

   (b) What is meant by the white fleece of the lamb?

2. The silkworm is (a) a caterpillar, (b) a larva. Choose the correct option.

   (i) a   (ii) b   (iii) both a and b   (iv) neither a nor b.

3. Which of the following does not yield wool?

   (i) Yak   (ii) Camel   (iii) Goat   (iv) Woolly dog

4. What is meant by the following terms?

   (i) Rearing (ii) Shearing   (iii) Sericulture

5. Given below is a sequence of steps in the processing of wool. Which are the missing steps? Add them.

   Shearing, _____, sorting, _____, _____, _____.

6. Make sketches of the two stages in the life history of the silk moth which are directly related to the production of silk.

7. Out of the following, which are the two terms related to silk production?

   Sericulture, floriculture, moriculture, apiculture and silviculture.

   Hints: (i)   Silk production involves cultivation of mulberry leaves and rearing silkworms.

   (ii)   Scientific name of mulberry is **Morus alba**.

8. Match the words of Column I with those given in Column II:

Column I	Column II
1. Scouring	(a) Yields silk fibres
2. Mulberry leaves	(b) Wool yielding animal
3. Yak	(c) Food of silk worm
4. Cocoon	(d) Reeling
	(e) Cleaning sheared skin

9. Given below is a crossword puzzle based on this lesson. Use hints to fill in the blank spaces with letters that complete the words.

Down

(D) 1 : Thorough washing
2 : Animal fibre
3 : Long thread like structure

Across

(A) 1 : Keeps warm
2 : Its leaves are eaten by silkworms
3 : Hatches from egg of moth

Extended Learning — Activities and Projects

1.

Paheli wants to know the maximum length of continuous silk thread that can be obtained from a cocoon.

Find out for her.

2.

Boojho wants to know why caterpillars need to shed their skin when they grow bigger but we humans do not.

Do you have any idea?

3.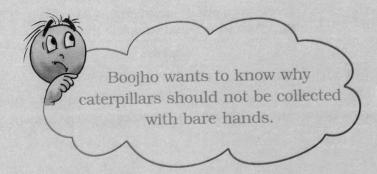

Boojho wants to know why caterpillars should not be collected with bare hands.

Can you help him?

4. Paheli wanted to buy a silk frock and went to the market with her mother. There they found that the artificial (synthetic) silk was much cheaper and wanted to know why. Do you know why? Find out.

5. Someone told Paheli that an animal called 'Vicuna' also gives wool. Can you tell her where this animal is found? Look for this in a dictionary or an encyclopaedia.

6. When handloom and textile exhibitions are held, certain stalls display real moths of various varieties of silk and their life histories. Try and visit these stalls with elders or teachers and see these moths and stages of their life history.

7. Look for eggs of any moth or butterfly in your garden or park or any other place full of plants. They look like tiny specks (dots) laid in a cluster on the leaves. Pull out the leaves containing eggs and place them in a cardboard box. Take some leaves of the same plant or another plant of the same variety, chop them and put them in the box. Eggs will hatch into caterpillars, which are busy eating day and night. Add leaves everyday for them to feed upon. Sometimes you may be able to collect the caterpillars. **But be careful**. Use a paper napkin or a paper to hold a caterpillar.

Observe everyday. Note the (i) number of days taken for eggs to hatch, (ii) number of days taken to reach the cocoon stage, and (iii) number of days to complete life cycle. Record your observations in your notebook.

You can read more on the following website:

www.indiansilk.kar.nic.in/

Did you know?

In terms of the number of sheep, India ranks third in the world, behind China and Australia. However, the New Zealand sheep are known to yield the best wool.

4 | Heat

In Chapter 3 you learnt that woollen clothes are made from animal fibres. You also know that cotton clothes are made from plant fibres. We wear woollen clothes during winters when it is cold outside. Woollen clothes keep us warm. We prefer to wear light coloured cotton clothes when it is hot. These give us a feeling of coolness. You might have wondered why particular types of clothes are suitable for a particular season.

In winter you feel cold inside the house. If you come out in the sun, you feel warm. In summer, you feel hot even inside the house. How do we know whether an object is hot or cold? How do we find out how hot or cold an object is? In this chapter we shall try to seek answers to some of these questions.

4.1 HOT AND COLD

In our day-to-day life, we come across a number of objects. Some of them are hot and some of them are cold. Tea is hot and ice is cold. List some objects you use commonly in Table 4.1. Mark these objects as hot or cold.

> Do not touch objects which are too hot. Be careful while handling a candle flame or a stove.

We see that some objects are cold while some are hot. You also know that some objects are hotter than others while some are colder than others. How do we decide which object is hotter than the other? We often do it by touching the objects. But is our sense of touch reliable? Let us find out.

Activity 4.1

Take three large mugs. Label them as A, B and C. Put cold water in mug A and hot water in mug B. Mix some cold

> Make sure that water is not so hot that you burn your hand

Table 4.1: Hot and cold objects

Object	Cold/Cool	Warm/Hot
Ice cream	√	
Spoon in a tea cup		
Fruit juice		
Handle of a frying pan		

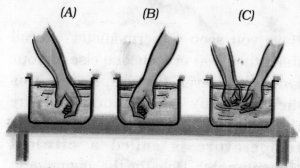

Fig. 4.1 *Feeling water in three mugs*

and hot water in mug C. Now dip your left hand in mug A and the right hand in mug B. After keeping the hands in the two mugs for 2–3 minutes, put both the hands simultaneously in mug C (Fig. 4.1). Do both the hands get the same feeling?

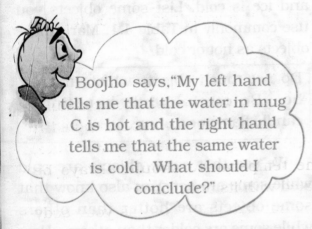

Boojho says, "My left hand tells me that the water in mug C is hot and the right hand tells me that the same water is cold. What should I conclude?"

Boojho's confusion shows that we cannot always rely on our sense of touch to decide whether an object is hot or cold. Sometimes it may deceive us.

Then, how do we find out how hot an object really is? A reliable measure of the hotness of an object is its **temperature**. Temperature is measured by a device called **thermometer**.

4.2 MEASURING TEMPERATURE

Have you seen a thermometer? Recall that when you or someone else in your family had fever, the temperature was measured by a thermometer. The thermometer that measures our body temperature is called a **clinical thermometer**. Hold the thermometer in

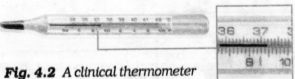

Fig. 4.2 *A clinical thermometer*

your hand and examine it carefully. If you do not have a thermometer, request a friend to share it with you. A clinical thermometer looks like the one shown in Fig. 4.2.

A clinical thermometer consists of a long, narrow, uniform glass tube. It has a bulb at one end. This bulb contains mercury. Outside the bulb, a small shining thread of mercury can be seen.

If you do not see the mercury thread, rotate the thermometer a bit till you see it. You will also find a scale on the thermometer. The scale we use is the celsius scale, indicated by °C.

Boojho wondered which of the two scales shown in Fig. 4.2 he should read. Paheli told him that India has adopted the celsius scale and we should read that scale. The other scale with the range 94–108 degrees is the Fahrenheit scale (°F). It was in use earlier.

A clinical thermometer reads temperature from 35°C to 42°C.

Activity 4.2

Reading a thermometer

Let us learn how to read a thermometer. First, note the temperature difference indicated between the two bigger marks. Also note down the number of divisions

- Thermometer should be washed before and after use, preferably with an antiseptic solution.
- Ensure that before use the mercury level is below 35°C.
- Read the thermometer keeping the level of mercury along the line of sight. (See Fig. 4.3).
- Handle the thermometer with care. If it hits against some hard object, it can break.
- Don't hold the thermometer by the bulb while reading it.

(shown by smaller marks) between these marks. Suppose the bigger marks read one degree and there are five divisions between them. Then, one small division can read $\frac{1}{5} = 0.2$ °C.

Wash the thermometer, preferably with an antiseptic solution. Hold it firmly and give it a few jerks. The jerks will bring the level of mercury down. Ensure that it falls below 35°C. Now place the bulb of the thermometer under your tongue. After one minute, take the thermometer out and note the reading. This is your body temperature. The temperature should always be stated with its unit. °C.

What did you record as your body temperature?

The normal temperature of human body is 37°C. Note that the temperature is stated with its unit.

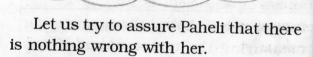

Paheli measured her body temperature. She got worried as it was not exactly 37°C.

Let us try to assure Paheli that there is nothing wrong with her.

Activity 4.3

Measure the body temperature of some of your friends (at least 10) with a

Fig. 4.3 *Correct method of reading a clinical thermometer*

Table 4.2: Body temperature of some persons

Name	Temperature (°C)

clinical thermometer. Record your observations as in Table 4.2.

Is the body temperature of every person 37°C?

The temperature of every person may not be 37°C. It could be slightly higher or slightly lower. Actually, what we call normal temperature is the average body temperature of a large number of healthy persons.

The clinical thermometer is designed to measure the temperature of human body only. The temperature of human body normally does not go below 35°C or above 42°C. That is the reason that this thermometer has the range 35°C to 42°C.

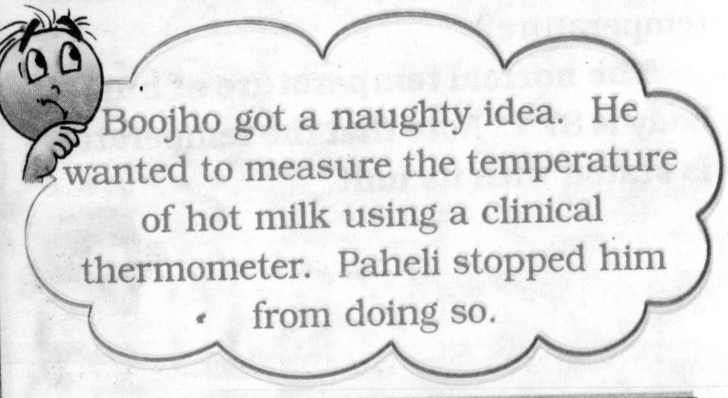

Boojho got a naughty idea. He wanted to measure the temperature of hot milk using a clinical thermometer. Paheli stopped him from doing so.

CAUTION

Do not use a clinical thermometer for measuring the temperature of any object other than the human body. Also avoid keeping the thermometer in the sun or near a flame. It may break.

4.3 LABORATORY THERMOMETER

How do we measure the temperature of other objects? For this purpose, there are other thermometers. One such thermometer is known as the laboratory thermometer. The teacher will show you

Different types of thermometers are used for different purposes. The maximum and minimum temperatures of the previous day, reported in weather reports, are measured by a thermometer called the maximum-minimum thermometer.

this thermometer. Look at it carefully and note the highest and the lowest temperature it can measure. The range of a laboratory thermometer is generally from –10°C to 110°C (Fig. 4.4). Also, as you did in the case of the clinical thermometer, find out how much a small division on this thermometer reads. You would need this information to read the thermometer correctly.

Let us now learn how this thermometer is used.

Activity 4.4

Take some tap water in a beaker or a mug. Dip the thermometer in water so that the bulb is immersed in water but does not touch the bottom or the sides of the container. Hold the thermometer vertically (Fig. 4.5). Observe the movement of mercury in the thermometer. Wait till the mercury thread becomes steady.

Fig. 4.4 A laboratory thermometer

In addition to the precautions needed while reading a clinical thermometer, the laboratory thermometer

- should be kept upright not tilted. (Fig. 4.5)
- bulb should be surrounded from all sides by the substance of which the temperature is to be measured. The bulb should not touch the surface of the container.

Fig. 4.5 *Measuring temperature of water with a laboratory thermometer*

Note the reading. This is the temperature of water at that time.

Compare the temperature of water recorded by each student in the class.

Are there any variations in the readings? Discuss the possible reasons. Let us try to answer this question.

Activity 4.5

Take some hot water in a beaker or a mug. Dip the thermometer in water. Wait till the mercury thread becomes steady and note the temperature. Now take out the thermometer from water. Observe carefully what happens now. Do you notice that as soon as you take the thermometer out of water, the level of mercury begins to fall. This means that the temperature must be read while the thermometer is in water.

You may recall that while taking your own temperature, you have to take the thermometer out of your mouth to note the reading. Can you then use the laboratory thermometer to measure your

Boojho now understand why clinical thermometer cannot be used to measure high temperatures. But still wonders whether a laboratory thermometer can be used to measure his body temperature.

Boojho wonders why the level of mercury should change at all when the bulb of the thermometer is brought in contact with another object?

body temperature? Obviously, it is not convenient to use the laboratory thermometer for this purpose.

Why does the mercury not fall or rise in a clinical thermometer when taken out of the mouth?

Observe a clinical thermometer again. Do you see a kink near the bulb (Fig. 4.6).

What is the use of the kink? It prevents mercury level from falling on its own.

Fig. 4.6 *A clinical thermometer has a kink in it*

There is a lot of concern over the use of mercury in thermometers. Mercury is a toxic substance and is very difficult to dispose of if a thermometer breaks. These days, digital thermometers are available which do not use mercury.

4.4 TRANSFER OF HEAT

You might have observed that a frying pan becomes hot when kept on a flame. It is because the heat passes from the flame to the utensil. When the pan is removed from the fire, it slowly cools down. Why does it cool down? The heat is transferred from the pan to the surroundings. So you can understand that in both cases, the heat flows from a hotter object to a colder object. In fact,

Paheli asks: "Does it mean that heat will not be transferred if the temperature of two objects is the same?"

in all cases heat flows from a hotter object to a colder object.

How does heat flow? Let us investigate.

Activity 4.6

Take a rod or flat strip of a metal, say of aluminium or iron. Fix a few small wax pieces on the rod. These pieces should be at nearly equal distances (Fig. 4.7). Clamp the rod to a stand. If you do not find a stand, you can put one end of the rod in between bricks. Now, heat the other end of the rod and observe.

What happens to the wax pieces? Do these pieces begin to fall? Which piece falls the first? Do you think that heat is

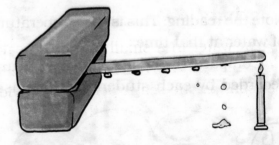

Fig. 4.7 *Flow of heat through a metal strip*

transferred from the end nearest to the flame to the other end?

The process by which heat is transferred from the hotter end to the colder end of an object is known as **conduction**. In solids, generally, the

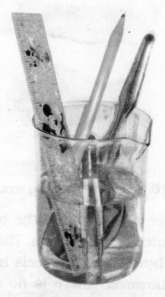

Fig. 4.8 *Conduction of heat by different materials*

heat is transferred by the process of conduction.

Do all substances conduct heat easily? You must have observed that the metallic pan for cooking has a plastic or wooden handle. Can you lift a hot pan by holding it from the handle without getting hurt?

Activity 4.7

Heat water in a small pan or a beaker. Collect some articles such as a steel spoon, plastic scale, pencil and divider. Dip one end of each of these articles in hot water (Fig. 4.8). Wait for a few

Table 4.3

Article	Material with which the article is made of	Does the other end get hot Yes/No
Steel spoon	Metal	Yes

minutes. Touch the other end. Enter your observation in Table 4.3.

The materials which allow heat to pass through them easily are **conductors** of heat. For examples, aluminum, iron and copper. The materials which do not allow heat to pass through them easily are poor conductors of heat such as plastic and wood. Poor conductors are known as **insulators**.

The water and air are poor conductors of heat. Then, how does the heat transfer take place in these substances? Let us find out.

Activity 4.8

Take a round bottom flask (if flask is not available, a beaker can be used). Fill it two-thirds with water. Place it on a tripod, or make some arrangement to place the flask in such a way that you can heat it by placing a candle below it. Wait till the water in the flask is still. Place a crystal of potassium permanganate at the bottom of the flask gently using a straw. Now, heat the water by placing the candle just below the crystal.

Write your observation in your notebook and also draw a picture of what you observe (Fig. 4.9).

When water is heated, the water near the flame gets hot. Hot water rises up. The cold water from the sides moves down towards the source of heat. This water also gets hot and rises

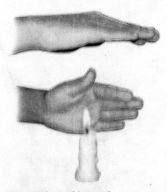

Fig. 4.10 *Transfer of heat by convection in air*

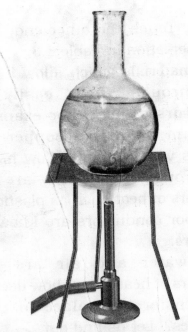

Fig. 4.9 Convection of heat in water

and water from the sides moves down. This process continues till the whole water gets heated. This mode of heat transfer is known as **convection.**

How does the heat travel in air? In which direction does the smoke go?

The air near the heat source gets hot and rises. The air from the sides comes in to take its place. In this way the air gets heated. The following activity confirms this idea.

Activity 4.9

Light a candle. Keep one hand above the flame and one hand on the side of the flame (Fig. 4.10). Do your hands feel equally hot? If not which hand feels hotter? And why?

Be careful. Keep your hands at a safe distance from the flame so that they do not get burnt.

Notice that towards the top, the air gets heated by convection. Therefore, the hand above the flame feels hot. On the sides, however, there is no convection and air does not feel as hot as at the top.

The people living in the coastal areas experience an interesting phenomenon. During the day, the land gets heated faster than the water. The air over the land becomes hotter and rises up. The cooler air from the sea rushes in towards the land to take its place. The warm air from the land moves towards the sea to complete the cycle. The air from the sea is called the **sea breeze**. To receive the cooler sea breeze, the windows of the houses in coastal areas are made to face the sea. At night it is exactly the reverse (Fig. 4.11). The water cools down more slowly than the land. So, the cool air from the land moves towards the sea. This is called the **land breeze**. Fig. 4.11 shows this phenomenon.

When we come out in the sun, we feel warm. How does the heat from the sun reach us? It cannot reach us by conduction or convection as there is no medium such as air in most part of the

Day time

Cool

Hot

Night time

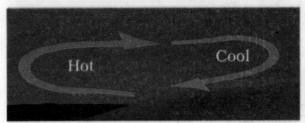

Hot

Cool

Fig. 4.11 *Land breeze and sea breeze*

space between the earth and the sun. From the sun the heat comes to us by another process known as **radiation**. The transfer of heat by radiation does not require any medium. It can take place whether a medium is present or not. When we sit in front of a room heater, we get heat by this process. A hot utensil kept away from the flame cools down as it transfers heat to the surroundings by radiation. Our body too, gives heat to the surroundings and receives heat from it by radiation.

All hot bodies radiate heat. When this heat falls on some object, a part of it is reflected, a part is absorbed and a part may be transmitted. The temperature of the object increases due to the absorbed part of the heat. Why

are you advised to use an umbrella when you go out in the sun?

4.5 KINDS OF CLOTHES WE WEAR IN SUMMER AND WINTER

You know that in summer we prefer light-coloured clothes and in winter we usually wear dark-coloured clothes. Why is it so? Let us find out

Activity 4.10

Take two identical tin cans. Paint the outer surface of one black and of the other white (Fig. 4.12). Pour equal amounts of water in each and leave them in the mid-day sun for about an hour. Measure the temperature of water in both the cans. Do you find any difference in the temperatures? In

We often use electricity and fuels like coal and wood to keep our houses cool or warm. Is it possible to construct buildings, that are not affected much by heat and cold outside? This can be done by constructing outer walls of buildings so that they have trapped layers of air. One way of doing this is to use hollow bricks, which are available these days.

Fig. 4.12 *Containers with black and white surface*

which can is the water warmer? You can feel the difference even by touching water in the two cans.

Activity 4.11

Fill the two cans used in Activity 4.10 with the same amount of hot water at the same temperature (say, at 60°C). Leave the cans in a room or in a shade. Note the temperature of water after 10–15 minutes. Does the temperature of water in both the cans fall by the same amount?

Do these activities suggest to you the reason why it is more comfortable to wear white or light-coloured clothes in the summer and dark-coloured clothes in the winter? Dark surfaces absorb more heat and, therefore, we feel comfortable with dark coloured clothes in the winter. Light coloured clothes reflect most of the heat that falls on them and, therefore, we feel more comfortable wearing them in the summer.

Woollen clothes keep us warm in winter

In the winter, we use woollen clothes. Wool is a poor conductor of heat. Moreover, there is air trapped in between the wool fibres. This air prevents the flow of heat from our body to the cold surroundings. So, we feel warm.

Suppose you are given the choice in winter of using either one thick blanket or two thin blankets joined together. What would you choose and why? Remember that there would be a layer of air in between the blankets.

Keywords

Celsius scale	Insulator	Sea breeze
Conduction	Land breeze	Temperature
Conductor	Radiation	Thermometer
Convection		

What you have learnt

- Our sense of touch is not always a reliable guide to the degree of hotness of an object.

- Temperature is a measure of the degree of hotness of an object.

- Thermometer is a device used for measuring temperatures.

- Clinical thermometer is used to measure our body temperature. The range of this thermometer is from 35°C to 42°C. For other purposes, we use the laboratory thermometers. The range of these thermometers is usually from –10°C to 110°C.

- The normal temperature of the human body is 37°C.

- The heat flows from a body at a higher temperature to a body at a lower temperature. There are three ways in which heat can flow from one object to another. These are conduction, convection and radiation.

- In solids, generally, the heat is transferred by conduction. In liquids and gases the heat is transferred by convection. No medium is required for transfer of heat by radiation.

- The materials which allow heat to pass through them easily are conductors of heat.

- The materials which do not allow heat to pass through them easily are called insulators.

- Dark-coloured objects absorb radiation better than the light-coloured objects. That is the reason we feel more comfortable in light-coloured clothes in the summer.

- Woollen clothes keep us warm during winter. It is so because wool is a poor conductor of heat and it has air trapped in between the fibres.

Exercises

1. State similarities and differences between the laboratory thermometer and the clinical thermometer.

2. Give two examples each of conductors and insulators of heat.

3. Fill in the blanks :

   (a) The hotness of an object is determined by its _____.

   (b) Temperature of boiling water cannot be measured by a _____ thermometer.

   (c) Temperature is measured in degree _____.

(d) No medium is required for transfer of heat by the process of _____.

(e) A cold steel spoon is dipped in a cup of hot milk. It transfers heat to its other end by the process of _____.

(f) Clothes of _____ colours absorb heat better than clothes of light colours.

4. Match the following :

(i) Land breeze blows during   (a) summer

(ii) Sea breeze blows during   (b) winter

(iii) Dark coloured clothes are preferred during   (c) day

(iv) Light coloured clothes are preferred during   (d) night

5. Discuss why wearing more layers of clothing during winter keeps us warmer than wearing just one thick piece of clothing .

6. Look at Fig. 4.13. Mark where the heat is being transferred by conduction, by convection and by radiation.

Fig. 4.13

7. In places of hot climate it is advised that the outer walls of houses be painted white. Explain.

8. One litre of water at 30°C is mixed with one litre of water at 50°C. The temperature of the mixture will be

(a) 80°C   (b) more than 50°C but less than 80°C

(c) 20°C   (d) between 30°C and 50°C

9. An iron ball at 40°C is dropped in a mug containing water at 40°C. The heat will

    (a)   flow from iron ball to water.

    (b)   not flow from iron ball to water or from water to iron ball.

    (c)   flow from water to iron ball.

    (d)   increase the temperature of both.

10. A wooden spoon is dipped in a cup of ice cream. Its other end

    (a)   becomes cold by the process of conduction.

    (b)   becomes cold by the process of convection.

    (c)   becomes cold by the process of radiation.

    (d)   does not become cold.

11. Stainless steel pans are usually provided with copper bottoms. The reason for this could be that

    (a)   copper bottom makes the pan more durable.

    (b)   such pans appear colourful.

    (c)   copper is a better conductor of heat than the stainless steel.

    (d)   copper is easier to clean than the stainless steel.

Extended Learning — Activities and Projects

1. Go to a doctor or your nearest health centre. Observe the doctor taking temperature of patients. Enquire:

    (a)   why she dips the thermometer in a liquid before use.

    (b)   why the thermometer is kept under the tongue.

    (c)   whether the body temperature can be measured by keeping the thermometer at some place other than the mouth.

    (d)   whether the temperature of different parts of the body is the same or different.

You can add more questions which come to your mind.

2. Go to a veterinary doctor (a doctor who treats animals). Discuss and find out the normal temperature of domestic animals and birds.

3. Wrap a thin paper strip tightly around an iron rod. Try to burn the paper with candle while rotating the iron rod continuously. Does it burn? Explain your observation.

4. Take a sheet of paper. Draw a spiral on it as shown in the Fig. 4.14. Cut out the paper along the line. Suspend the paper as shown in Fig. 4.14 above a lighted candle. Observe what happens. Think of an explanation.

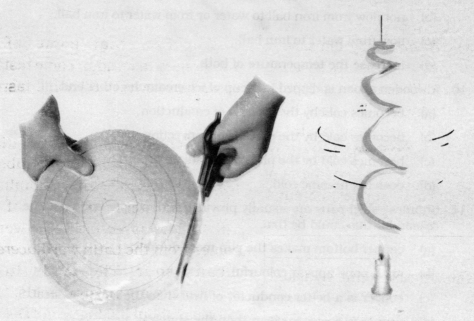

Fig. 4.14

5. Take two similar transparent glass bottles having wide mouths. Put a few crystals of potassium permanganate or pour a few drops of ink in one bottle. Fill this bottle with hot water. Fill the other bottle with cold water. Cover the cold water bottle with a thick piece of paper such as a postcard. Press the postcard firmly with one hand and hold the bottle with the other hand. Invert the bottle and place it on top of the hot water bottle. Hold both the bottles firmly. Ask some other person to pull the postcard. Observe what happens. Explain.

You can read more on the following website:

www.bbc.co.uk/schools/gcsebitesize/physics/energy/ energytransferrev6.shtml

Did you know?

The celsius scale was devised by a Swedish astronomer, Anders Celsius in 1742. Strangely, he fixed the temperature of the boiling water as 0°C and of freezing water as 100°C. However, this order was reversed very soon.

5 Acids, Bases and Salts

We use in our daily life a large number of substances such as lemon, tamarind, common salt, sugar and vinegar. Do they have the same taste? Let us recall tastes of some edible substances listed in Table 5.1. If you have not tasted any of these substances taste it now and enter the result in Table 5.1.

CAUTION
1. Do not taste anything unless asked to do so.
2. Do not touch anything unless asked to do so.

Table 5.1

Substance	Taste (sour/bitter/any other)
Lemon juice	
Orange juice	
Vinegar	
Curd	
Tamarind (*imli*)	
Sugar	
Common salt	
Amla	
Baking soda	
Grapes	
Unripe mango	

You find that some of these substances taste sour, some taste bitter, some taste sweet and some taste salty.

5.1 ACIDS AND BASES

Curd, lemon juice, orange juice and vinegar taste sour. These substances taste sour because they contain **acids**. The chemical nature of such substances is **acidic**. The word acid comes from the Latin word *acere* which means sour. The acids in these substances are natural acids.

What about baking soda? Does it also taste sour? If not, what is its taste? Since, it does not taste sour it means, that it has no acids in it. It is bitter in taste. If you rub its solution between fingers, it feels soapy. Substances like these which are bitter in taste and feel soapy on touching are known as **bases**. The nature of such substances is said to be **basic**.

If we cannot taste every substance, how do we find its nature?

Special type of substances are used to test whether a substance is acidic or basic. These substances are known as **indicators**. The indicators change their colour when added to a solution containing an acidic or a basic substance. Turmeric, litmus, china rose petals (*Gudhal*), etc., are some of the naturally occurring indicators.

Do you know?	
Name of acid	**Found in**
Acetic acid	Vinegar
Formic acid	Ant's sting
Citric acid	Citrus fruits such as oranges, lemons, etc.
Lactic acid	Curd
Oxalic acid	Spinach
Ascorbic acid (Vitamin C)	*Amla*, Citrus fruits
Tartaric acid	Tamarind, grapes, unripe mangoes, etc.

All the acids mentioned
above occur in nature

Name of base	**Found in**
Calcium hydroxide	Lime water
Ammonium hydroxide	Window cleaner
Sodium hydroxide/ Potassium hydroxide	Soap
Magnesium hydroxide	Milk of magnesia

5.2 NATURAL INDICATORS AROUND Us

Litmus: A natural dye

The most commonly used natural indicator is litmus. It is extracted from **lichens** (Fig. 5.1). It has a mauve (purple) colour in distilled water. When added to an acidic solution, it turns red and when added to a basic solution, it turns blue. It is available in the form of a solution, or in the form of strips of paper, known as litmus paper. Generally, it is **available as red and blue litmus paper** (Fig. 5.1).

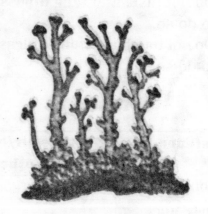

(a)

(b)

Fig. 5.1 (a) Lichens, and (b) Red and blue litmus paper

Can I taste all substances to find their taste?

No. Have you not read the caution? We should not taste unknown substances. They could harm us.

Activity 5.1

▪ Mix some water with lemon juice in a plastic cup/tumbler/test tube.

▪ Put a drop of the above solution on a strip of the red litmus paper with the help of a dropper.

Is there any change in colour?

▪ Repeat the same exercise with the blue litmus paper.

Note down if there is any change in colour.

Perform the same activity with the following substances:

Tap water, detergent solution, aerated drink, soap solution, shampoo, common salt solution, sugar solution, vinegar, baking soda solution, milk of magnesia, washing soda solution, lime water. If possible make solutions in distilled water.

Record your observations as in Table. 5.2.

In your Table, are there any substances on which litmus had no effect? Name those substances.

The solutions which do not change the colour of either red or blue litmus are known as **neutral** solutions. These substances are neither acidic nor basic.

Fig. 5.2 *Children performing litmus test*

Turmeric is another natural indicator

Activity 5.2

▪ Take a tablespoonful of turmeric powder. Add a little water and make a paste.

▪ Make turmeric paper by depositing turmeric paste on blotting paper/filter paper and drying it. Cut thin strips of the yellow paper obtained.

▪ Put a drop of soap solution on the strip of turmeric paper.

What do you observe?

To prepare limewater, dissolve some lime (*chuna*) in water in a bottle. Stir the solution and keep it for some time. Pour a little from the top. This is lime water.

Table 5.2

S. No.	Test solution	Effect on red litmus paper	Effect on blue litmus paper	Inference

You can prepare a card for your mother on her birthday. Apply turmeric paste on a sheet of plane white paper and dry it. Draw a beautiful flower with soap solution with the help of a cotton bud. You will get a beautiful greeting card.

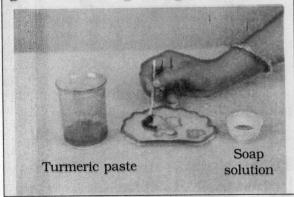

Turmeric paste   Soap solution

Similarly test the solutions listed in Table 5.3 and note down your observations. You may try solutions of other substances also.

China Rose as Indicator

Activity 5.3

Collect some China rose (*Gudhal*) petals and place them in a beaker. Add some

Now I understand why a turmeric stain on my white shirt is turned to red when it is washed with soap. It is because the soap solution is basic.

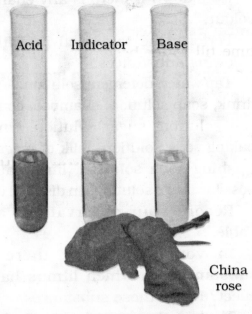

Acid   Indicator   Base

China rose

Fig. 5.3 *China rose flower and indicator prepared from it*

Table 5.3

S. No.	Test solution	Effect on turmeric solution	Remarks
1.	Lemon juice		
2.	Orange juice		
3.	Vinegar		
4.	Milk of magnesia		
5.	Baking soda		
6.	Lime water		
7.	Sugar		
8.	Common salt		

Table 5.4

S. No.	Test solution	Initial colour	Final colour
1.	Shampoo (dilute solution)		
2.	Lemon juice		
3.	Soda water		
4.	Sodium hydrogencarbonate solution		
5.	Vinegar		
6.	Sugar solution		
7.	Common salt solution		

warm water. Keep the mixture for some time till water becomes coloured. Use the coloured water as an indicator. Add five drops of the indicator to each of the solutions given in Table 5.4.

What is the effect of the indicator on acidic, basic and neutral solutions? China rose indicator (Fig. 5.3) turns acidic solutions to dark pink (magenta) and basic solutions to green.

I am not getting the same result when using solid baking soda on dry litmus paper. Why?

Make a solution of baking soda and then try.

Paheli brought the following paheli (riddle) for you.

Coffee is brown
And bitter in taste.
Is it an acid?
Or a base?
Don't give the answer
Without any test,
You are in the dark
With its taste.

Activity 5.4

The teacher is requested to get the following dilute chemicals from his/her school laboratory or from a nearby school: hydrochloric acid, sulphuric acid, nitric acid, acetic acid, sodium hydroxide, ammonium hydroxide, calcium hydroxide (lime water).

Table 5.5

S. No.	Name of acid	Effect on litmus paper	Effect on turmeric paper	Effect on China rose solution
1.	Dilute hydrochloric acid			
2.				
3.				

Are you familiar with the term acid rain? Have you ever heard about damaging effect of acid rain? As the name indicates the rain containing excess of acids is called an acid rain. Where do these acids come from? The rain becomes acidic because carbon dioxide, sulphur dioxide and nitrogen dioxide (which are released into the air as pollutants) dissolve in rain drops to form carbonic acid, sulphuric acid and nitric acid respectively. Acid rain can cause damage to buildings, historical monuments, plants and animals.

CAUTION

Great care should be taken while handling laboratory acids and bases because these are corrosive in nature, irritating and harmful to skin.

Demonstrate the effect of the three indicators on each of these solutions. Record your observations in Table 5.5.

5.3 NEUTRALISATION

We have learnt that acids turn blue litmus red and bases turn red litmus blue. Let us see what happens when an acid is mixed with a base.

We are going to use an indicator you have not used so far. It is called **phenolphthalein**.

Activity 5.5

To be demonstrated by the teacher in the class

Fill one fourth of a test tube with dilute hydrochloric acid. Note down its colour. Note down the colour of phenolphthalein solution also. Add 2–3 drops of the indicator to the acid. Now shake the test tube gently. Do you observe any change in colour of the acid?

Add to the acidic solution a drop of sodium hydroxide solution by a dropper.

Stir the tube gently. Is there any change in the colour of the solution? Continue adding the sodium hydroxide solution drop by drop while stirring till the pink colour just appears.

Now add one more drop of dilute hydrochloric acid. What do you observe? The solution again becomes colourless. Again add one drop of sodium hydroxide solution. Is there any change in colour? The solution again becomes pink in colour.

It is evident that when the solution is basic, phenolphthalein gives a pink colour. On the other hand, when the solution is acidic, it remains colourless.

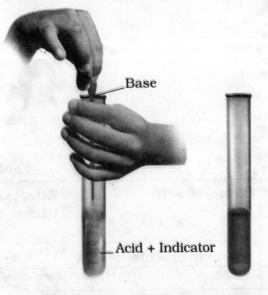

Fig. 5.4 *Process of neutralisation*

When an acidic solution is mixed with a basic solution, both the solutions neutralise the effect of each other. When an acid solution and a base solution are mixed in suitable amounts, both the acidic nature of the acid and the basic nature of the base are destroyed. The resulting solution is neither acidic nor basic. Touch the test tube immediately after neutralisation. What do you observe? In neutralisation reaction, heat is always produced, or evolved. The evolved heat raises the temperature of the reaction mixture.

In neutralisation reaction a new substance is formed. This is called **salt**. Salt may be acidic, basic or neutral in nature. Thus, neutralisation can be defined as follows:

The reaction between an acid and a base is known as neutralisation. Salt and water are produced in this process with the evolution of heat.

Acid+Base → Salt+Water
(Heat is evolved)

The following reaction is an example:
Hydrochloric acid (HCl) + Sodium hydroxide (NaOH) →
Sodium chloride (NaCl) + Water (H_2O)
Boojho added dilute sulphuric acid to lime water. Will the reaction mixture become hot or cool?

5.4 Neutralisations in Everyday Life

Indigestion

Our stomach contains hydrochloric acid. It helps us to digest food, as you have learnt in Chapter 2. But too much of acid in the stomach causes indigestion. Sometimes indigestion is painful. To relieve indigestion, we take an antacid such as milk of magnesia, which contains magnesium hydroxide. It neutralises the effect of excessive acid.

Ant bite

When an ant bites, it injects the acidic liquid (formic acid) into the skin. The effect of the acid can be neutralised by rubbing moist baking soda (sodium hydrogen carbonate) or calamine solution, which contains zinc carbonate.

Soil treatment

Excessive use of chemical fertilisers makes the soil acidic. Plants do not grow well when the soil is either too **acidic** or too **basic**. When the soil is too acidic, it is treated with bases like quick lime (calcium oxide) or slaked lime (calcium hydroxide). If the soil is basic, organic matter is added to it. Organic matter releases acids which neutralises the basic nature of the soil.

Factory wastes

The wastes of many factories contain acids. If they are allowed to flow into the water bodies, the acids will kill fish and other organisms. The factory wastes are, therefore, neutralised by adding basic substances.

Keywords

Acid	Basic	Neutralisation
Acidic	Indicator	Salt
Base	Neutral	

What you have learnt

- Acids are sour in taste. Bases are bitter in taste and soapy to touch.

- Acid turns blue litmus red. Bases turn red litmus blue.

- Substances which are neither acidic nor basic are called neutral.

- Solutions of substances that show different colour in acidic, basic and neutral solutions are called indicators.

- An acid and a base neutralise each other and form a salt. A salt may be acidic, basic or neutral in nature.

Exercises

1. State differences between acids and bases.

2. Ammonia is found in many household products, such as window cleaners. It turns red litmus blue. What is its nature?

3. Name the source from which litmus solution is obtained. What is the use of this solution?

4. Is the distilled water acidic/basic/neutral? How would you verify it?

5. Describe the process of neutralisation with the help of an example.

6. Mark 'T' if the statement is true and 'F' if it is false:

   (i) Nitric acid turn red litmus blue. (T/F)

   (ii) Sodium hydroxide turns blue litmus red. (T/F)

   (iii) Sodium hydroxide and hydrochloric acid neutralise each other and form salt and water. (T/F)

   (iv) Indicator is a substance which shows different colours in acidic and basic solutions. (T/F)

   (v) Tooth decay is caused by the presence of a base. (T/F)

7. Dorji has a few bottles of soft drink in his restaurant. But, unfortunately, these are not labelled. He has to serve the drinks on the demand of customers. One customer wants acidic drink, another wants basic and third one wants neutral drink. How will Dorji decide which drink is to be served to whom?

8. Explain why:

   (a) An antacid tablet is taken when you suffer from acidity.

(b) Calamine solution is applied on the skin when an ant bites.

(c) Factory waste is neutralised before disposing it into the water bodies.

9. Three liquids are given to you. One is hydrochloric acid, another is sodium hydroxide and third is a sugar solution. How will you identify them? You have only turmeric indicator.

10. Blue litmus paper is dipped in a solution. It remains blue. What is the nature of the solution? Explain.

11. Consider the following statements:

(a) Both acids and bases change colour of all indicators.

(b) If an indicator gives a colour change with an acid, it does not give a change with a base.

(c) If an indicator changes colour with a base, it does not change colour with an acid.

(d) Change of colour in an acid and a base depends on the type of the indicator.

Which of these statements are correct?

(i) All four   (ii) a and d   (iii) b and c   (iv) only d

Extended Learning — Activities and Projects

1. Using the knowledge of acids and bases, write a secret message with the help of baking soda and beet root. Explain how it works.

   (**Hint:** Prepare baking soda solution in water. Use this solution to write the message on a sheet of white paper with a cotton bud. Rub a slice of fresh beet root over the message.)

2. Prepare red cabbage juice by boiling a piece of red cabbage in water. Use it as an indicator and test the acidic and basic solutions with it. Present your observations in the form of a table.

3. Bring the soil sample of your area, find out if it is acidic, basic or neutral. Discuss with farmers if they treat the soil in any manner.

4. Visit a doctor. Find out the medicines, he prescribes to treat acidity. Ask him how acidity can be prevented.

Did you know?

Each cell in our body contains an acid, the **deoxyribonucleic acid** or **DNA**. It controls every feature of the body such as our looks, colour of our eyes, our height etc. Proteins that build part of our cells are also made of **amino acids**. The fats in our body contain **fatty acids**.

6 Physical and Chemical Changes

Every day you come across many changes in your surroundings. These changes may involve one or more substances. For example, your mother may ask you to dissolve sugar in water to make a cold drink. Making a sugar solution is a change. Similarly, setting curd from milk is a change. Sometimes milk becomes sour. Souring of milk is a change. Stretched rubber band also represents a change.

Make a list of ten changes you have noticed around you.

In this chapter we shall perform some activities and study the nature of these changes. Broadly, these changes are of two kinds, **physical** and **chemical**.

Fig. 6.1 *Paper pieces*

6.1 PHYSICAL CHANGES

Activity 6.1

Cut a piece of paper in four square pieces. Cut each square piece further into four square pieces. Lay these pieces on the floor or a table so that the pieces acquire the shape of the original piece of paper (Fig. 6.1).

Obviously, you cannot join the pieces back to make the original piece, but is there a change in the property of the paper?

Activity 6.2

Collect the chalk dust lying on the floor near the blackboard in your classroom. Or, crush a small piece of chalk into dust. Add a little water to the dust to make a paste. Roll it into the shape of a piece of chalk. Let it dry.

Did you recover chalk from the dust?

Activity 6.3

Take some ice in a glass or plastic tumbler. Melt a small portion of ice by placing the tumbler in the sun. You have now a mixture of ice and water. Now place the tumbler in a freezing mixture (ice plus common salt).

Does the water become solid ice once again?

Activity 6.4

Boil some water in a container. Do you see the steam rising from the surface of water? Hold an inverted pan by its handle over the steam at some distance from the boiling water. Observe the inner surface of the pan.

Do you see any droplet of water there?

Activity 6.5

CAUTION
Be careful while handling a flame.

Hold a used hack-saw blade with a pair of tongs. Keep the tip of the free end on the flame of a gas stove. Wait for a few minutes.

Does the colour of the tip of the blade change?

Remove the blade from the flame. Observe the tip once again after some time.

Does it get back its original colour?

In Activities 6.1 and 6.2 above, you saw that paper and a piece of chalk underwent changes in size. In Activities 6.3 and 6.4, water changed its state (from solid to liquid, or from gas to liquid). In Activity 6.5, the hack-saw blade changed colour on heating.

Properties such as shape, size, colour and state of a substance are called its **physical properties**. A change in which a substance undergoes a change in its physical properties is called a **physical change.** A physical change is generally reversible. **In such a change no new substance is formed**.

Let us now consider the other kind of change.

6.2 CHEMICAL CHANGE

A change with which you are quite familiar is the rusting of iron. If you leave a piece of iron in the open for some time, it acquires a film of brownish substance. This substance is called **rust** and the process is called **rusting** (Fig. 6.2). Iron gates of parks or farmlands, iron benches kept in lawns and gardens, almost every article of iron, kept in the open gets rusted. At home you must have seen shovels and spades getting rusted when exposed to the

Fig. 6.2 *Rusting iron*

atmosphere for some time. In the kitchen, a wet iron pan (*tawa*) often gets rusted if left in that state for some time. Rust is not iron. It is different from iron on which it gets deposited.

Let us consider a few more changes where new substances are formed.

Activity 6.6

(To be demonstrated by the teacher)

CAUTION
It is dangerous to look for long at the burning magnesium ribbon. The teachers should advise children not to stare at the burning ribbon.

Get a small piece of a thin strip or ribbon of magnesium. Clean its tip with sandpaper. Bring the tip near a candle flame. It burns with a brilliant white

Fig. 6.3 *Magnesium ribbon burning*

light (Fig. 6.3). When it is completely burnt it leaves behind a powdery ash.

Does the ash look like the magnesium ribbon?

The change can be represented by the following equation:

Magnesium (Mg) + Oxygen (O_2) → Magnesium oxide (MgO)

The equations here are different from those in mathematics. In equations of this kind, the arrow implies 'becomes'. No attempt should be made to balance chemical equations at this stage.

Collect the ash and mix it with a small amount of water. Stir the mixture (aqueous solution) well. Test the mixture with blue and red litmus papers.

Does the mixture turn red litmus blue?

Does the mixture turn blue litmus red?

On the basis of this test, how do you classify the aqueous solution — acidic or basic?

On dissolving the ash in water it forms a new substance. This change can be written in the form of the following equation:

Magnesium oxide (MgO) + Water (H_2O) → Magnesium hydroxide [Mg(OH)$_2$]

As you have already learnt in Chapter 5, magnesium hydroxide is a base. So, magnesium oxide is a new substance formed on burning of magnesium. Magnesium hydroxide is another new substance formed by mixing magnesium oxide with water.

Activity 6.7

(To be demonstrated by the teacher)
Dissolve about a teaspoonful of copper sulphate (blue vitriol or *neela thotha*) in about half a cup of water in a glass tumbler or a beaker. Add a few drops of dilute sulphuric acid to the solution. You should get a blue coloured solution. Save a small sample of the solution in a test tube or a small glass bottle. Drop a nail or a used shaving blade into the remaining solution. Wait for half an hour or so. Observe the colour of the solution. Compare it with the colour of the sample solution saved separately (Fig. 6.4).

colour of the solution from blue to green is due to the formation of iron sulphat   a new substance. The brown deposi'   n the iron nail is copper, another new substance. We can write the reaction as:

Copper sulphate solution (blue) + Iron → Iron sulphate solution (green) + Copper (brown deposit)

Activity 6.8

Take about a teaspoonful of vinegar in a test tube. Add a pinch of baking soda to it. You would hear a hissing sound and see bubbles of a gas coming out. Pass this gas through freshly prepared lime water as shown in Fig. 6.5.

What happens to the lime water?

Copper sulphate

Iron sulphate

Fig. 6.4 *Change in colour of the copper sulphate solution due to reaction with iron*

Do you see any change in the colour of the solution?

Take out the nail or the blade.

Has it changed in any way?

The changes that you notice are due to a reaction between copper sulphate and iron. The change of

The change in the test tube is as follows:

Vinegar (Acetic acid) + Baking soda (Sodium hydrogencarbonate) →

Carbon dioxide + other substances

The reaction between carbon dioxide and lime water is as follows:

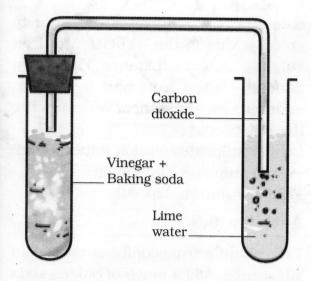

Fig. 6.5 *Set up to pass gas through lime water*

Carbon dioxide (CO_2) + Lime water [$Ca(OH)_2$] → Calcium Carbonate ($CaCO_3$) + Water (H_2O)

When carbon dioxide is passed through lime water, calcium carbonate is formed, which makes lime water milky. The turning of lime water into milky is a standard test of carbon dioxide. You will use it in Chapter 10 to show that the air we breathe out is rich in carbon dioxide.

In Activities 6.6–6.8, you saw that in each change one or more new substances were formed. In Activity 6.6, the ash was the new substance formed when magnesium was burnt. In Activity 6.7, the reaction of copper sulphate with iron produced iron sulphate and copper. Both of these are new substances. Copper was deposited on the shaving blade of iron. In Activity 6.8, vinegar and baking soda together produced carbon dioxide, which turned lime water milky. Can you name the new substance formed in this reaction?

A change in which one or more new substances are formed is called a chemical change. A chemical change is also called a **chemical reaction**.

Chemical changes are very important in our lives. All new substances are formed as a result of chemical changes. For example, if a metal is to be extracted from an ore, such as iron from iron ore, we need to carry out a series of chemical changes. A medicine is the end product of a chain of chemical reactions. Useful new materials, such as plastics and detergents, are produced by chemical reactions. Indeed, every new material is discovered by studying chemical changes.

We have seen that one or more new substances are produced in a chemical change. In addition to new products, the following may accompany a chemical change:

- Heat, light or any other radiation (ultraviolet, for example) may be given off or absorbed.
- Sound may be produced.
- A change in smell may take place or a new smell may be given off.
- A colour change may take place .
- A gas may be formed.

Let us look at some examples.

You saw that burning of magnesium ribbon is a chemical change. Burning of coal, wood or leaves is also a chemical change. In fact, burning of any substance is a chemical change. Burning is always accompanied by production of heat.

Explosion of a firework is a chemical change. You know that such an explosion produces heat, light, sound and unpleasant gases that pollute the atmosphere. That is why you are advised not to play with fireworks.

When food gets spoiled, it pro[d] a foul smell. Shall we call this ch chemical change?

You must have noticed that a s. an apple acquires a brown colour if it not consumed immediately. If you have not seen this change in colour, cut a fresh slice of apple and keep it away for some time. Repeat the same activity with a slice of potato or brinjal. The change of colour in these cases is due to the formation of new substances. Are not these changes chemical changes?

In Chapter 5, you neutralised an acid with a base. Is neutralisation a chemical change?

A protective shield

You must have heard of the ozone layer in our atmosphere. It protects us from the harmful ultraviolet radiation which come from the sun. Ozone absorbs this radiation and breaks down to oxygen. Oxygen is different from ozone. Can we call the breaking down of ozone a chemical change?

If ultraviolet radiation were not absorbed by ozone, it would reach the earth's surface and cause harm to us and other life forms. Ozone acts as a natural shield against this radiation.

We learnt in Chapter 1 that plants produce their food by a process called photosynthesis. Can we call photosynthesis a chemical change?

Paheli said that even digestion is a chemical change.

6.3 Rusting of Iron

Let us get back to rusting. This is one change that affects iron articles and slowly destroys them. Since iron is used in making bridges, ships, cars, truck bodies and many other articles, the monetary loss due to rusting is huge.

The process of rusting can be represented by the following equation:

Iron (Fe) + Oxygen (O_2, from the air) + water (H_2O) → rust (iron oxide Fe_2O_3)

For rusting, the presence of both oxygen and water (or water vapour) is essential.

In fact, if the content of moisture in air is high, which means if it is more humid, rusting becomes faster.

So, how do we prevent rusting? Prevent iron articles from coming in contact with oxygen, or water, or both. One simple way is to apply a coat of paint or grease. In fact, these coats should be applied regularly to prevent rusting. Another way is to deposit a layer of a metal like chromium or zinc on iron.

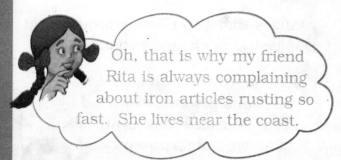

Oh, that is why my friend Rita is always complaining about iron articles rusting so fast. She lives near the coast.

This process of depositing a layer of zinc on iron is called **galvanisation**. The iron pipes we use in our homes to carry water are galvanised to prevent rusting.

You know that ships are made of iron and a part of them remains under water. On the part above water also, water drops keep clinging to the ship's outer surface. Moreover, the water of the sea contains many salts. The salt water makes the process of rust formation faster. Therefore, ships suffer a lot of damage from rusting in spite of being

Stainless steel is made by mixing iron with carbon and metals like chromium, nickel and manganese. It does not rust.

painted. So much so, that a fraction of ship's iron has to be replaced every year. Can you imagine the monetary loss to the world?

6.4 CRYSTALLISATION

In Class VI you have learnt that salt can be obtained by the evaporation of sea water. The salt obtained in this manner is not pure and its crystals are small. The shape of the crystals cannot be seen clearly. However, large crystals of pure substances can be formed from their solutions. The process is called **crystallisation**. It is an example of a physical change.

Activity 6.9

(To be performed in the presence of the teacher)

CAUTION
Use only dilute sulphuric acid. Be careful while boiling water.

Take a cupful of water in a beaker and add a few drops of dilute sulphuric acid. Heat the water. When it starts boiling add copper sulphate powder slowly while stirring continuously (Fig. 6.6). Continue adding copper sulphate powder till no more powder can be dissolved. Filter the solution. Allow it to cool. Do not disturb the solution when it is cooling. Look at the solution after some time. Can you see the crystals of copper sulphate? If not, wait for some more time.

Copper sulphate

Crystals

Fig. 6.6 *Crystals of copper sulphate*

You have learnt about physical and chemical changes. Try to identify changes that you observe around you as physical or chemical changes.

Keywords

Chemical change

Chemical reaction

Crystallisation

Galvanisation

Physical change

Rusting

What you have learnt

- Changes can be of two types, physical and chemical.
- Physical changes are changes in the physical properties of substances. No new substances are formed in these changes. These changes may be reversible.
- In chemical changes new substances are produced.
- Some substances can be obtained in pure state from their solutions by crystallisation.

Exercises

1. Classify the changes involved in the following processes as physical or chemical changes:

    (a) Photosynthesis

    (b) Dissolving sugar in water

    (c) Burning of coal

    (d) Melting of wax

    (e) Beating aluminium to make aluminium foil

    (f) Digestion of food

2. State whether the following statements are true or false. In case a statement is false, write the corrected statement in your notebook.

    (a) Cutting a log of wood into pieces is a chemical change. (True/False)

    (b) Formation of manure from leaves is a physical change. (True/False)

(c) Iron pipes coated with zinc do not get rusted easily. (True/False)

(d) Iron and rust are the same substances. (True/False)

(e) Condensation of steam is not a chemical change. (True/False)

3. Fill in the blanks in the following statements:

(a) When carbon dioxide is passed through lime water, it turns milky due to the formation of _____.

(b) The chemical name of baking soda is _____.

(c) Two methods by which rusting of iron can be prevented are _____ and _____.

(d) Changes in which only _____ properties of a substance change are called physical changes.

(e) Changes in which new substances are formed are called _____ changes.

4. When baking soda is mixed with lemon juice, bubbles are formed with the evolution of a gas. What type of change is it? Explain.

5. When a candle burns, both physical and chemical changes take place. Identify these changes. Give another example of a familiar process in which both the chemical and physical changes take place.

6. How would you show that setting of curd is a chemical change?

7. Explain why burning of wood and cutting it into small pieces are considered as two different types of changes.

8. Describe how crystals of copper sulphate are prepared.

9. Explain how painting of an iron gate prevents it from rusting.

10. Explain why rusting of iron objects is faster in coastal areas than in deserts.

11. The gas we use in the kitchen is called liquified petroleum gas (LPG). In the cylinder it exist as a liquid. When it comes out from the cylinder it becomes a gas (Change – A) then it burns (Change – B). The following statements pertain to these changes. Choose the correct one.

(i) Process – A is a chemical change.

(ii) Process – B is a chemical change.

(iii) Both processes A and B are chemical changes.

(iv) None of these processes is a chemical change.

12. Anaerobic bacteria digest animal waste and produce biogas (Change – A). The biogas is then burnt as fuel (Change – B). The following statements pertain to these changes. Choose the correct one.

(i) Process – A is a chemical change.

(ii) Process – B is a chemical change.

(iii)   Both processes A and B are chemical changes.

(iv)   None of these processes is a chemical change.

Extended Learning — Activities and Projects

1. Describe two changes that are harmful. Explain why you consider them harmful. How can you prevent them?

2. Take three glass bottles with wide mouths. Label them A, B and C. Fill about half of bottle A with ordinary tap water. Fill bottle B with water which has been boiled for several minutes, to the same level as in A. In bottle C, take the same boiled water and of the same amount as in other bottles. In each bottle put a few similar iron nails so that they are completely under water. Add a teaspoonful of cooking oil to the water in bottle C so that it forms a film on its surface. Put the bottles away for a few days. Take out nails from each bottle and observe them. Explain your observations.

3. Prepare crystals of alum.

4. Collect information about the types of fuels used for cooking in your area. Discuss with your teachers/parents/others which fuels are less polluting and why.

Did you know?

Near the Qutub Minar in Delhi stands an iron pillar (Fig. 6.7) which is more than 7 metres high. It weighs more than 6000 kg. It was built more than 1600 years ago. After such a long period it has not rusted. For its quality of rust resistance it has been examined by scientists from all parts of the world. It tells something about the advances India had made in metal technology as back as 1600 years ago.

Fig. 6.7 *Iron pillar*

7 Weather, Climate and Adaptations of Animals to Climate

Do you remember the things that you were asked to pack when you were heading for a hill station? When the sky is cloudy, your parents insist that you carry an umbrella. Have you heard elders in your family discuss the weather before planning a family function? You must have also heard the experts discussing the weather before the start of a game. Have you ever wondered why? The weather may have a profound effect on the game. It has a profound effect on our lives. Many of our daily activities are planned based on the weather predicted for that day. There are daily reports of the weather on the television and radio and in the newspapers. But do you know what this weather really is?

In this chapter, we will study about the weather and climate. We will also see how different forms of life are adapted to the climate of their habitat.

7.1 WEATHER

In Fig. 7.1 a sample of weather report from a newspaper is given.

We find that the daily weather report carries information about the temperature, humidity and rainfall during the past 24 hours. It also predicts the weather for the day. Humidity, as you might know, is a measure of the moisture in air.

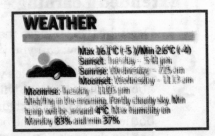

Fig. 7.1 *A sample of a weather report from a newspaper*

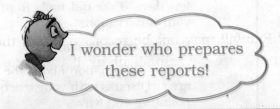

I wonder who prepares these reports!

The weather reports are prepared by the Meteorological Department of the Government. This department collects data on temperature, wind, etc., and makes the weather prediction.

Activity 7.1

Cut out the weather reports of the last week from any newspaper. If you do not get a newspaper at home borrow from your neighbours or friends and copy these reports in your notebook. You can also collect weather reports from a library. Paste all the cut-outs on a white sheet or on a chart paper.

Now record the information from the weather reports collected by you in Table 7.1. The first row is just a sample. Fill all the columns according to the data in the chart that you have prepared.

Table 7.1

Weather data of a week

Date	Max. temp. (°C)	Min. temp. (°C)	Min. humidity (%)	Max. humidity(%)	Rainfall* (mm)
23-08-06	36.2	27.8	54	82	

*(Rainfall may not be recorded for all the days since it may not rain everyday. Leave the space for rainfall blank if the data is not available.)

Rainfall is measured by an instrument called the rain gauge. It is basically a measuring cylinder with a funnel on top to collect rainwater.

Do all the seven days have the same maximum and minimum temperatures, humidity and rainfall? The maximum and minimum temperatures recorded may be the same for some of the days. However, all the parameters are not the same on any two days. Over a week there may be considerable variation. **The day-to-day condition of the atmosphere at a place with respect to the temperature, humidity, rainfall, wind-speed, etc., is called the weather at that place**. The temperature, humidity, and other factors are called the **elements** of the weather. The weather of a place changes day after day and week after week. That is why we often say, "today's weather is too humid", or "the weather was warm last week".

The weather is such a complex phenomenon that it can vary over very short periods of time. It can happen sometimes that it is sunny in the morning, but suddenly clouds appear from nowhere and it starts raining heavily. Or, a heavy rain may vanish in a matter of minutes and give way to bright sunshine. You must have had several such experiences. Try to recall any such experience and share it with your friends. Since weather is such a complex phenomenon, it is not easy to predict.

Look at the graph given below which shows the maximum temperature recorded during 03 August 2006 to 09 August 2006 at Shillong, Meghalaya (Fig. 7.2).

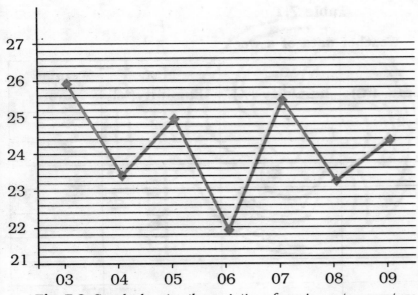

Date	Maximum temperature
03-08-06	26.0°C
04-08-06	23.5°C
05-08-06	25.0°C
06-08-06	22.0°C
07-08-06	25.5°C
08-08-06	23.3°C
09-08-06	24.4°C

Fig. 7.2 *Graph showing the variation of maximum temperature during 03 to 09 August 2006*

As it is clear from any weather report, the maximum and minimum temperatures are recorded every day. Do you know how these temperatures are recorded. In Chapter 4 you have learnt that there are special thermometers for this purpose, called **maximum and minimum thermometers**. Can you guess when during the day we have the maximum temperature and when the minimum?

The maximum temperature of the day occurs generally in the afternoon while the minimum temperature occurs generally in the early morning. Can you now understand why in summers we feel so miserable in the afternoon and comparatively comfortable early in the morning?

I wonder why weather changes so frequently!

What is the source of weather in the first place?

All changes in the weather are caused by the **sun**. The sun is a huge sphere of hot gases at a very high temperature. The distance of the sun from us is very large. Even then the energy sent out by the sun is so huge that it is the source of all heat and light on the earth. So, the sun is the primary source of energy that causes changes in the weather. Energy absorbed and reflected by the earth's surface, oceans and the atmosphere play important roles in determining the weather at any place. If you live near the sea, you would have realised that the weather at your place is different from that of a place in a desert, or near a mountain.

What about the times of sunrise and sunset? You know that in winters it becomes dark early and you do not get much time to play. Are the days shorter in winter than in summer? Try to find it out yourself by completing the project given at the end of the chapter.

7.2 CLIMATE

Meteorologists record the weather every day. The records of the weather have been preserved for the past several decades. These help us to determine the weather pattern at a place. **The average weather pattern taken over a long time, say 25 years, is called the climate of the place.** If we find that the temperature at a place is high most of the time, then we say that the climate of that place is hot. If there is also heavy rainfall on most of the days in the same place, then we can say that the climate of that place is hot and wet.

In Table 7.2 and 7.3, we have given the climatic condition at two places in India. The mean temperature for a given month is found in two steps. First we find the average of the temperatures recorded during the month. Second, we calculate the average of such average temperatures over many years. That gives the mean temperature. The two places are: Srinagar in Jammu and Kashmir, and Thiruvananthapuram in Kerala.

Table 7.2 Srinagar (Jammu & Kashmir)

Information about climate

Month	Mean temperature °C		Mean total rainfall (mm)
	Daily minimum	Daily maximum	
Jan	-2.3	4.7	57
Feb	-0.6	7.8	65
Mar	3.8	13.6	99
Apr	7.7	19.4	88
May	10.7	23.8	72
Jun	14.7	29.2	37
July	8.2	30.0	49
Aug	17.5	29.7	70
Sep	12.9	27.8	33
Oct	6.1	21.9	36
Nov	0.9	14.7	27
Dec	-1.6	8.2	43

Table 7.3 Thiruvananthapuram (Kerala)

Information about climate

Month	Mean temperature °C		Mean total rainfall (mm)
	Daily minimum	Daily maximum	
Jan	22.2	31.5	23
Feb	22.8	31.9	24
Mar	24.1	32.6	40
Apr	24.9	32.6	117
May	24.7	31.6	230
Jun	23.5	29.7	321
July	23.1	29.2	227
Aug	23.2	29.4	138
Sep	23.3	30.0	175
Oct	23.3	29.9	282
Nov	23.1	30.3	185
Dec	22.6	31.0	66

(Note: The numbers for the mean total rainfall have been rounded off)

By looking at Tables 7.2 and 7.3 we can easily see the difference in the climate of Jammu & Kashmir and Kerala. We can see that Kerala is very hot and wet in comparison to Jammu & Kashmir, which has a moderately hot and wet climate for a part of the year.

Similar data for the western region of India, for example Rajasthan, will show that the temperature is high during most part of the year. But during winter, which lasts only for a few months, the temperature is quite low. This region receives very little rainfall. This is the typical desert climate. It is **hot and dry.** The north-eastern India receives rain for a major part of the year. Therefore, we can say that the climate of the north-east is **wet**.

7.3 CLIMATE AND ADAPTATION

Climate has a profound effect on all living organisms.

Animals are adapted to survive in the conditions in which they live. Animals living in very cold and hot climate must possess special features to protect themselves against the extreme cold or heat. Recall from Chapter 9 of your Class VI science book the definition of adaptation. Features and habits that help animals to adapt to their surroundings are a result of the process of evolution.

In Chapter 9 you will learn about the effect of weather and climate on soil. Here we will study the effect of climate on animals only. In Class VI, you have read about adaptations of animals to certain habitats. As examples of adaptation of animals to climatic conditions, we discuss only animals living in polar regions and tropical rainforests.

As the name suggests, the polar regions are situated near the poles, i.e., north pole and south pole.

Some well-known countries that belong to the polar regions are Canada, Greenland, Iceland, Norway, Sweden, Finland, Alaska in U.S.A. and Siberian region of Russia.

Examples of some countries where the tropical rainforests are found are India, Malaysia, Indonesia, Brazil, Republic of Congo, Kenya, Uganda, and Nigeria.

Activity 7.2

Take an outline map of the world. Mark the polar regions in blue. Similarly, mark the tropical regions in red.

(i) The polar regions

The polar regions present an extreme climate. These regions are covered with snow and it is very cold for most part of the year. For six months the sun does not set at the poles while for the other six months the sun does not rise. In winters, the temperature can be as low as –37°C. Animals living there have adapted to these severe conditions. Let us see how they are adapted by considering the examples of polar bears and penguins.

Polar bears have white fur so that they are not easily visible in the snowy white background. It protects them from their predators. It also helps them in catching their prey. To protect them from extreme cold, they have two thick layers of fur. They also have a layer of fat under their skin. In fact, they are so well-insulated that they have to move slowly and rest often to avoid getting overheated.

Physical activities on warm days necessitate cooling. So, the polar bear goes for swimming. It is a good swimmer. Its paws are wide and large, which help it not only to swim well but also walk with ease in the snow. While swimming under water, it can close its nostrils and can remain under water for long durations. It has a strong sense of smell so that it can catch its prey for food. We can understand the adaptations of polar bears with the help of the flow chart shown in Fig. 7.3.

Another well-known animal living in the polar regions is the penguin (Fig. 7.4). It is also white and merges well with the white background. It also has a thick skin and a lot of fat to protect it from cold. You may have seen pictures of penguins huddled together. This they do to keep warm. Recall how warm you feel when you are in a hall full of people.

Fig. 7.4 *Penguins huddled together*

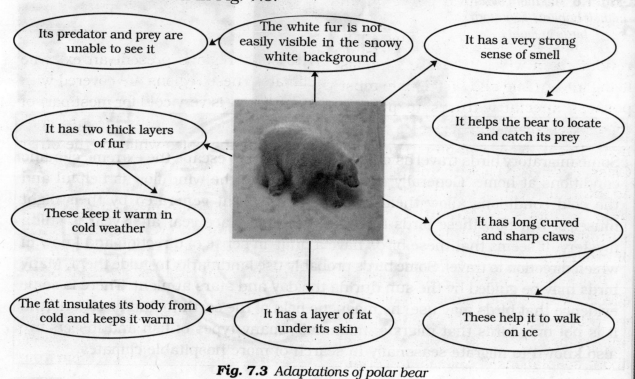

Fig. 7.3 *Adaptations of polar bear*

Its predator and prey are unable to see it

The white fur is not easily visible in the snowy white background

It has a very strong sense of smell

It has two thick layers of fur

It helps the bear to locate and catch its prey

These keep it warm in cold weather

It has long curved and sharp claws

The fat insulates its body from cold and keeps it warm

It has a layer of fat under its skin

These help it to walk on ice

Fig. 7.5 *Feet of penguin*

Like polar bears, penguins are also good swimmers. Their bodies are streamlined and their feet have webs, making them good swimmers (Fig. 7.5).

Other animals living in the polar regions are many types of fishes, musk oxen, reindeers, foxes, seals, whales, and birds. It is to be noted that while fish can remain under cold water for long, birds must remain warm to survive. They migrate to warmer regions when winter sets in. They come back after the winter is over. You know probably that India is one of the destinations of many of these birds. You must have seen or heard about the Siberian crane that comes from Siberia to places like Bharatpur in Rajasthan and Sultanpur in Haryana, and some

Do fishes and butterflies also migrate like birds?

Fig. 7.6 *Migratory birds in their habitat/ Migratory birds in flight*

Did you know?

Some migratory birds travel as much as 15000 km to escape the extreme climatic conditions at home. Generally they fly high where the wind flow is helpful and the cold conditions allow them to disperse the heat generated by their flight muscles. But how these birds travel to the same place year after year is still a mystery. It seems that these birds have a built–in sense of direction and know in which direction to travel. Some birds probably use landmarks to guide them. Many birds may be guided by the sun during the day and stars at night. There is some evidence that birds may use the magnetic field of the earth to find direction. And it is not only birds that migrate; mammals, many types of fish and insects are also known to migrate seasonally in search of more hospitable climates.

wetlands of north east and some other parts of India (Fig. 7.6).

(ii) The tropical rainforests

The tropical region has generally a hot climate because of its location around the equator. Even in the coldest month the temperature is generally higher than about 15°C. During hot summers, the temperature may cross 40°C. Days and nights are almost equal in length throughout the year. These regions get plenty of rainfall. An important feature of this region is the tropical rainforests. Tropical rainforests are found in Western Ghats and Assam in India, Southeast Asia, Central America and Central Africa. Because of continuous warmth and rain, this region supports wide variety of plants and animals. The major types of animals living in the rainforests are monkeys, apes, gorillas, tigers, elephants, leopards, lizards, snakes, birds and insects.

Let us read about the adaptations of these animals to a hot, humid climate.

The climatic conditions in rainforests are highly suitable for supporting an enormous number and a variety of animals.

Since the numbers are large, there is intense competition for food and shelter. Many animals are adapted to living on the trees. Red-eyed frog (Fig. 7.7) has developed sticky pads on its feet to help it climb trees on which it lives. To help them live on the trees, monkeys (Fig. 7.8) have long tails for grasping branches. Their hands and feet

Fig. 7.7 *Red-eyed frog*

Fig. 7.8 *A new world monkey*

are such that they can easily hold on to the branches.

As there is competition for food, some animals are adapted to get food not easily reachable. A striking example is that of the bird Toucan (Fig. 7.9), which possesses a long, large beak. This helps a toucan to reach the fruits on branches which are otherwise too weak to support its weight.

Many tropical animals have sensitive hearing, sharp eyesight, thick skin and a skin colour which helps them to camouflage by blending with the surroundings. This is to protect them from predators. For example, big cats

Fig. 7.9 Toucan   **Fig. 7.10** Lion-tailed macaque

(lions and tigers) have thick skins and sensitive hearing.

The lion-tailed macaque (also called Beard ape) lives in the rainforests of Western Ghats (Fig. 7.10). Its most outstanding feature is the silver-white mane, which surrounds the head from the cheeks down to its chin. It is a good climber and spends a major part of its life on the tree. It feeds mainly on fruits. It also eats seeds, young leaves, stems, flowers and buds. This beard ape also searches for insects under the bark of the trees. Since it is able to get sufficient food on the trees, it rarely comes down on the ground.

Another well-known animal of Indian tropical rainforest is the elephant (Fig. 7.11). It has adapted to the conditions of rainforests in many remarkable ways. Look at its trunk. It uses it as a nose because of which it has a strong sense of smell. The trunk is also used by it for picking up food. Moreover, its tusks are modified teeth. These can tear the bark of trees that elephant loves to eat. So, the elephant is able to handle the competition for food rather well. Large ears of the elephant help it to hear even very soft sounds. They also help the elephant to keep cool in the hot and humid climate of the rainforest.

Fig. 7.11 An Indian elephant

Keywords

Adaptation	Maximum temperature	Tropical rainforest
Climate	Migration	Tropical region
Elements of weather	Minimum temperature	Weather
Humidity	Polar region	

What you have learnt

- The day-to-day condition of the atmosphere at a place with respect to the temperature, humidity, rainfall, wind-speed, etc., is called the weather at that place.

- The weather is generally not the same on any two days and week after week.

- The maximum temperature of the day occurs generally in the afternoon while the minimum temperature occurs in the early morning.

- The times of sunrise and sunset also change during the year.

- All the changes in the weather are driven by the sun.

- The average weather pattern taken over a long time, say 25 years, is called the climate of the place.

- The tropical and the polar regions are the two regions of the earth, which have severe climatic conditions.

- Animals are adapted to the conditions in which they live.

- The polar regions are very cold throughout the year. The sun does not set for six months in a year and in the other six months it does not rise.

- Animals in the polar region are adapted to the extremely cold climate by having some special characteristics such as white fur, strong sense of smell, a layer of fat under the skin, wide and large paws for swimming and walking, etc.

- Migration is another means to escape the harsh, cold conditions.

- Because of the hospitable climatic conditions huge populations of plants and animals are found in the tropical rainforests.

- Animals in the tropical rainforests are adapted such that they eat different kinds of food to overcome the competition for food and shelter.

- Some adaptations of animals living in the tropical rainforests include living on the trees, development of strong tails, long and large beaks, bright colours, sharp patterns, loud voice, diet of fruits, sensitive hearing, sharp eyesight, thick skin, ability to camouflage in order to protect themselves from predators, etc.

Exercises

1. Name the elements that determine the weather of a place.

2. When are the maximum and minimum temperature likely to occur during the day?

3. Fill in the blanks:

    (i)   The average weather taken over a long time is called _____.

(ii) A place receives very little rainfall and the temperature is high throughout the year, the climate of that place will be _____ and _____ .

(iii) The two regions of the earth with extreme climatic conditions are _____ and _____.

4. Indicate the type of climate of the following areas:

(a) Jammu and Kashmir: _____

(b) Kerala: _____

(c) Rajasthan: _____

(d) North-east India: _____

5. Which of the two changes frequently, weather or climate?

6. Following are some of the characteristics of animals:

(i)	Diets heavy on fruits	(ii)	White fur
(iii)	Need to migrate	(iv)	Loud voice
(v)	Sticky pads on feet	(vi)	Layer of fat under skin
(vii)	Wide and large paws	(viii)	Bright colours
(ix)	Strong tails	(x)	Long and large beak

For each characteristic indicate whether it is adaptation for tropical rainforests or polar regions. Do you think that some of these characteristics can be adapted for both regions?

7. The tropical rainforest has a large population of animals. Explain why it is so.

8. Explain, with examples, why we find animals of certain kind living in particular climatic conditions.

9. How do elephant living in the tropical rainforest adapt itself.

Choose the correct option which answers the following question:

10. A carnivore with stripes on its body moves very fast while catching its prey. It is likely to be found in

(i) polar regions   (ii) deserts

(iii) oceans   (iv) tropical rainforests

11. Which features adapt polar bears to live in extremely cold climate?

(i) A white fur, fat below skin, keen sense of smell.

(ii) Thin skin, large eyes, a white fur.

(iii) A long tail, strong claws, white large paws.

(iv) White body, paws for swimming, gills for respiration.

12. Which option best describes a tropical region?

    (i)   hot and humid

    (ii) moderate temperature, heavy rainfall

    (iii) cold and humid

    (iv) hot and dry

Extended Learning — Projects and Activities

1. Collect weather reports of seven successive days in the winter months (preferably December). Collect similar reports for the summer months (preferably June). Now prepare a table for sunrise and sunset times as shown:

Table

June			December		
Date	Sunrise	Sunset	Date	Sunrise	Sunset

Try to answer the following questions:

    (i)   Is there any difference in the time of sunrise during summer and winter?

    (ii) When do you find that the sun rises earlier?

    (iii) Do you also find any difference in the time of sunset during the month of June and December?

    (iv) When are the days longer?

    (v) When are the nights longer?

    (vi) Why are the days sometimes longer and sometimes shorter?

    (vii) Plot the length of the day against the days chosen in June and December.

(Instructions for plotting graphs are given in Chapter 13.)

2. Collect information about the Indian Meteorological Department. If possible visit its website: *http//www.imd.gov.in.*

Write a breif report about the things this department does.

Did you know?

Rainforests cover about 6% of the earth's surface, but they have more than half of the animal life and about two-thirds of the flowering plants of the planet. However, much of this life is still unknown to us.

8 Winds, Storms and Cyclones

Orissa was hit by a cyclone with wind speed of 200 km/h on 18 October 1999. The cyclone smashed 45,000 houses making 7,00,000 people homeless. On 29 October the same year, a second cyclone with wind speed of 260 km/h hit Orissa again. It was accompanied by water waves about 9 m high. Thousands of people lost their lives. Property worth crores of rupees was destroyed. The cyclone affected agriculture, transport, communication, and electricity supply.

Fig. 8.1 *Image taken by a satellite of a cyclone approaching the coast of Orissa*

Courtesy: India Meteorological Department, New Delhi

But, what are cyclones? How are they formed? Why are they so destructive? In this chapter we shall seek answers to some of these questions.

We begin with some activities involving air. These activities will clarify some basic features concerning a cyclone. Before we begin, remember that the moving air is called the **wind**.

8.1 AIR EXERTS PRESSURE

Activity 8.1

Whenever an activity involves heating, be very careful. It is advised that such activities are performed in the presence of an elderly person from your family. Or, carry out these activities in the presence of your teacher.

You need to boil water in the following activity.

Take a tin can with a lid. Fill it approximately half with water. Heat the can on a candle flame till the water boils. Let the water boil for a few minutes. Blow out the candle. Immediately put the lid tightly on the can. Be careful in handling the hot can. Put the can carefully in a shallow metallic vessel or a washbasin. Pour fresh water over the can. What happens to the shape of the can?

Fig. 8.2 *Can with hot water being cooled*

Can you guess why the shape of the can gets distorted?

If you cannot get a tin can, take a soft plastic bottle. Fill it with hot water. Empty the bottle and immediately cap it tightly. Place the bottle under running water.

Recall now some of your experiences.

When you fly a kite, does the wind coming from your back help?

If you are in a boat, is it easier to row it if there is wind coming from behind you?

Do you find it difficult to ride a bicycle against the direction of the wind.

You know that we have to fill air into the bicycle tube to keep it tight. Also, you know that a bicycle tube overfilled with air may burst. What is the air doing inside the tube?

Discuss with your friends how the air in the bicycle tube keeps it in shape.

All these experiences show that the air exerts pressure. It is due to this pressure that the leaves of trees, banners, or flags flutter when the wind

is blowing. You can list some more experiences which show that the air has pressure.

Let us now try to explain why the can (or the bottle) gets distorted. As water is poured over the can, some steam in the can condenses into water, reducing the amount of air inside. The pressure of air inside the can decreases than the pressure exerted by the air from outside the can. As a result the can gets compressed.

This activity again confirms that air exerts pressure.

8.2 HIGH SPEED WINDS ARE ACCOMPANIED BY REDUCED AIR PRESSURE

Activity 8.2

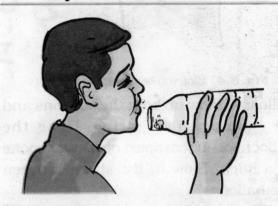

Fig. 8.3 *Blowing into the bottle*

Crumple a small piece of paper into a ball of size smaller than the mouth of an empty bottle. Hold the empty bottle on its side and place the paper ball just inside its mouth. Now try to blow on the ball to force it into the bottle. Try the activity with bottles of different sizes. Challenge your friends if they can force the paper ball in by blowing into the bottle.

Paheli and Boojho are thinking about the following question:

Why is it difficult to force the paper ball into the bottle?

Activity 8.3

Blow the balloons

Take two balloons of approximately equal size. Put a little water into the

Fig. 8.4 *Blowing between the balloons*

balloons. Blow up both the balloons and tie each one to a string. Hang the balloons 8–10 cm apart on a cycle spoke or a stick. Blow in the space between the balloons.

What did you expect? What happens?

Try different ways of blowing on the balloons to see what happens.

Activity 8.4

Can you blow and lift?

Hold a strip of paper, 20 cm long and 3 cm wide, between your thumb and forefinger as shown in the Fig. 8.5. Now blow over the paper.

Paheli thinks that the strip will be lifted up. Boojho thinks that the strip will bend down.

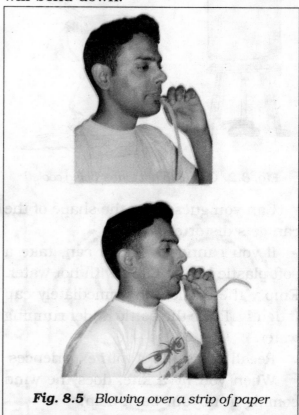

Fig. 8.5 *Blowing over a strip of paper*

What do you think will happen to the paper?

Let us try to understand the observations in Activities 8.2, 8.3 and 8.4.

Were the observations along the lines you thought? Do you get the feeling that the increased wind speed is accompanied by a reduced air pressure?

When we blow into the mouth of the bottle, the air near the mouth has higher speed. This decreases the pressure there. The air pressure inside the bottle is higher than near the mouth. The air inside the bottle pushes the ball out.

In Activity 8.3 you saw that when you blew between the balloons, they moved towards each other. How could this happen? This could happen if the pressure of air between the balloons were somehow reduced. The pressure outside the balloons would then push them towards each other.

In Activity 8.4 you saw that when you blew over the paper strip, it went upwards. Again, this could happen if blowing over the paper reduced the air pressure above the strip.

We see that the **increased wind speed is, indeed, accompanied by a reduced air pressure**.

Can you imagine what would happen if high-speed winds blew over the roofs of buildings? If the roofs were weak, they could be lifted and blown away. If you have any such experience, share it with your friends.

Let us try to understand how winds are produced, how they bring rain and how they can be destructive sometimes.

You already know that when air moves, it is called wind. **Air moves from the region where the air pressure is high to the region where the pressure is low.** The greater the difference in pressure, the faster the air moves. But how are the pressure differences created in nature? Is the difference in temperature involved? The following activities will help you to understand this.

8.3 AIR EXPANDS ON HEATING

Activity 8.5

Take a boiling tube. Stretch a balloon tightly over the neck of the tube. You can use a tape to make it tight. Pour some hot water in a beaker. Insert the boiling tube with the balloon in the hot water. Observe for 2–3 minutes for any change in shape of the balloon. Take the tube out, let it cool down to the room temperature. Take some ice-cold water in another beaker and place the tube with the balloon in cold water for 2–3 minutes. Observe the change in the shape of the balloon.

Think and try to answer:
What makes the balloon inflated when the boiling tube is placed in hot water?

Why is the same balloon deflated when the tube is kept in cold water?

Can we infer from the first observation that air expands on heating? Can you now state what happens to the air in the boiling tube when it cools down?

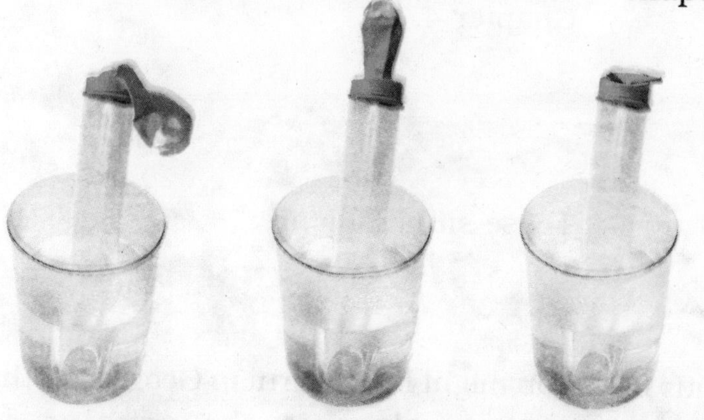

Balloon tied over the neck of the boiling tube

Boiling tube immersed in hot water

Boiling tube immersed in ice-cold water

Fig. 8.6 *The shape of the balloon in hot and cold water*

The next activity is very interesting. This will make you understand more about hot air.

Activity 8.6

Take two paper bags or empty paper cups of the same size. Hang the two bags in

CAUTION
Handle the burning candle carefully.

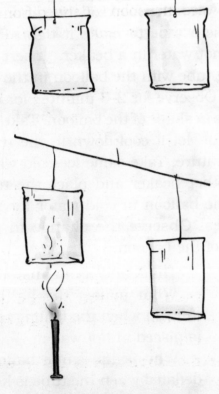

Fig. 8.7 *Hot air rising up*

the inverted position on the two ends of a metal or wooden stick.

Tie a piece of thread in the middle of the stick. Hold the stick by the thread (Fig. 8.7) as in a balance. Put a burning candle below one of the bags as shown in the figure. Observe what happens.

Why is the balance of the bags disturbed?

Does this activity indicate that warm air rises up? As the warm air rises up, it pushes the bag above the candle. Does the disturbance of the balance suggest that the warm air is lighter than the cold air?

Can you now explain why smoke always rises up?

Also, it is important to remember that on heating the air expands and occupies more space. When the same thing occupies more space, it becomes lighter. **The warm air is**, therefore, **lighter than the cold air**. That is the reason that the smoke goes up.

In nature there are several situations, where warm air rises at a place. The air pressure at that place is lowered. The cold air from the surrounding areas rushes in to fill its place. This sets up convection in air, as you learnt in Chapter 4.

8.4 Wind Currents are Generated Due to Uneven Heating on the Earth

These situations are:

(a) Uneven heating between the equator and the poles

You might have learnt in Geography that regions close to the equator get maximum heat from the Sun. The air in these regions gets warm. The warm air rises, and the cooler air from the regions in the 0–30 degrees latitude belt on either side of the equator moves in. These winds blow from the north and the south towards the equator. At the poles, the air is colder than that at latitudes about 60 degrees. The warm air at these latitudes rises up and the cold wind from the polar regions rushes in, to take its place. In this way, wind circulation is set up from the poles to the warmer latitudes, as shown in Fig. 8.8.

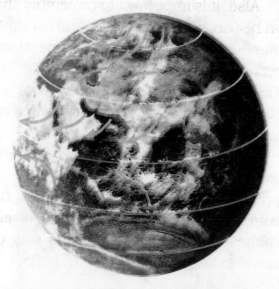

Fig. 8.8 *The wind flow pattern because of uneven heating on the earth*

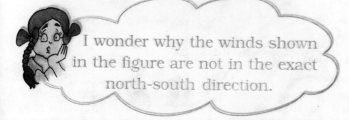
I wonder why the winds shown in the figure are not in the exact north-south direction.

The winds would have flown in the north-south direction from north to south, or from south to north. A change in direction is however, caused by the rotation of the earth.

(b) Uneven heating of land and water

You have read about the sea breeze and the land breeze in Chapter 4.

In summer, near the equator the land warms up faster and most of the time the temperature of the land is higher than that of water in the oceans. The air over the land gets heated and rises. This causes the winds to flow from the oceans towards the land. These are monsoon winds (Fig. 8.9).

> The word monsoon is derived from the Arabic word *'mausam'*, which means 'season'.

In winter, the direction of the wind flow gets reversed; it flows from the land to the ocean (Fig. 8.10).

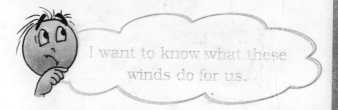
I want to know what these winds do for us.

The winds from the oceans carry water and bring rain. It is a part of the water cycle.

The monsoon winds carry water and it rains.

Clouds bring rain and give us happiness. Farmers in our country depend mainly on rains for their harvests. There are many folk songs associated with clouds and rain. Sing and enjoy with your friends, if you know such a song. Here is one for you.

Roaring clouds across the sky
Tell us that monsoon's here
Dark and floating clouds then pour
Raindrops every where.
Clouds make lightning flash overhead
And irrigate fields with rain
Clouds make earth, its fragrance spread
When wet with drops of rain.
Rising from the ocean vast
Clouds fill up with rain
Rain to ocean, back at last
To mingle with ocean again!

However, it is not always a happy ending. Rains often create problems.

Can you list some of the problems?

You can discuss the causes and solutions of the problems with your teacher and parents.

In nature itself there are certain situations that can sometimes create disasters and pose threat to humans, animals and plant life.

Let's study two such situations — **thunderstorms** and **cyclones**.

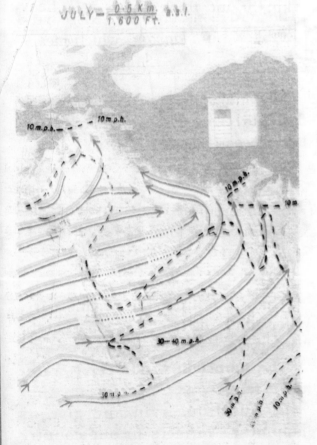

Fig. 8.9 *Uneven heating of land especially the Rajasthan desert generates monsoon winds from* **southwest** *direction in* **summer**. *These winds carry lots of water from the Indian Ocean.*

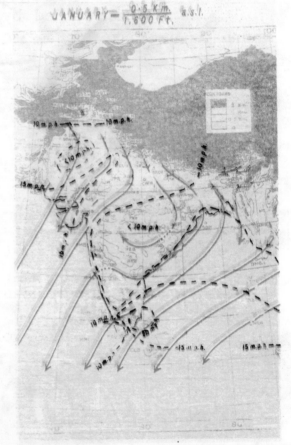

Fig. 8.10 *Uneven heating of land and water in* **winter** *generate winds from the* **northwest** *colder land. These colder winds carry little water, hence bring small amount of rain in winter.*

Courtesy: India Meteorological Department, New Delhi

8.5 THUNDERSTORMS AND CYCLONES

Thunderstorms develop in hot, humid tropical areas like India very frequently. The rising temperatures produce strong upward rising winds. These winds carry water droplets upwards, where they freeze, and fall down again. The swift movement of the falling water droplets along with the rising air create lightning and sound. It is this event that we call a **thunderstorm**. You will read about lightning in higher classes.

If a storm is accompanied by lightning, we must take the following precautions:

- Do not take shelter under an isolated tree. If you are in a forest take shelter under a small tree. Do not lie on the ground.
- Do not take shelter under an umbrella with a metallic end.
- Do not sit near a window. Open garages, storage sheds, metal sheds are not safe places to take shelter.
- A car or a bus is a safe place to take shelter.
- If you are in water, get out and go inside a building.

How a thunderstorm becomes a cyclone

You know that water requires heat when it changes from liquid to vapour state. Does the water give back heat when vapour condenses into liquid? Can you recall any experience to support this?

Structure of a cyclone

The centre of a cyclone is a calm area. It is called the **eye** of the storm. A large cyclone is a violently rotating mass of air in the atmosphere, 10 to 15 km high. The diameter of the eye varies from 10 to 30 km (Fig. 8.11). It is a region free of clouds and has light winds. Around this calm and clear eye (Fig. 8.12), there is a cloud region of about 150 km in size. In this region there are high-speed winds (150–250 km/h) and thick clouds with heavy rain. Away from this region the wind speed gradually decreases. The formation of a cyclone is a very complex process. A model is shown in Fig. 8.11.

Before cloud formation, water takes up heat from the atmosphere to change into vapour. When water vapour changes back to liquid form as raindrops, this heat is released to the atmosphere. The heat released to the atmosphere warms the air around. The air tends to rise and causes a drop in pressure. More air rushes to the centre of the storm. This cycle is repeated. The chain of events ends with the formation of a very low-pressure system with very high-speed winds revolving around it. It is this weather condition that we call a **cyclone.** Factors like wind speed, wind direction, temperature and humidity contribute to the development of cyclones.

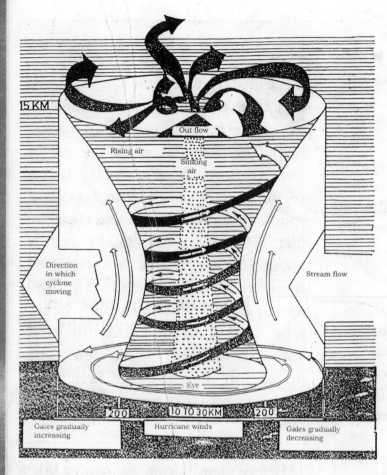

15 KM

Out flow

Rising air

Sinking air

Direction in which cyclone moving

Stream flow

Eye

200   10 TO 30KM   200

Gales gradually increasing

Hurricane winds

Gales gradually decreasing

Fig. 8.11 *Formation of a cyclone*

Fig. 8.12 *The image of the 'eye' of a cyclone*

Fig. 8.13 *Rising water caused by a cyclone.*

Courtesy: India Meteorological Department, New Delhi

8.6 DESTRUCTION CAUSED BY CYCLONES

Cyclones can be very destructive. Strong winds push water towards the shore even if the storm is hundreds of kilometres away. These are the first indications of an approaching cyclone. The water waves produced by the wind are so powerful that a person cannot overcome them.

The low pressure in the eye lifts water surface in the centre. The rising water may be as high as 3–12 metres (Fig. 8.13). It appears like a water-wall moving towards the shore. As a result, the seawater enters the low-lying coastal areas, causing severe loss of life and property. It also reduces the fertility of the soil.

Continuous heavy rainfall may further worsen the flood situation.

High-speed winds accompanying a cyclone can damage houses, telephones and other communication systems, trees, etc., causing tremendous loss of life and property.

A cyclone is known by different names in different parts of the world. It is called a **'hurricane'** in the American continent. In Philippines and Japan it is called a **'typhoon'** (Fig. 8.14).

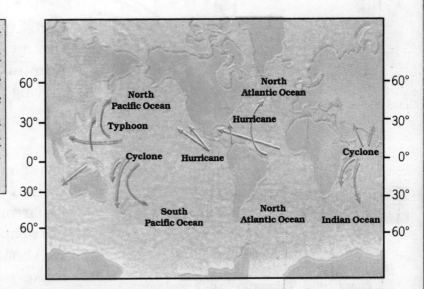

Fig. 8.14 Regions near the equator where cyclones form. Cyclones are worldwide phenomena.

The diameter of a tornado can be as small as a metre and as large as a km, or even wider. The funnel of a tornado sucks dust, debris and everything near it at the base (due to low pressure) and throws them out near the top. Here are a few accounts of the survivors of tornados-(from Discovery channel's "Young Discovery Series").

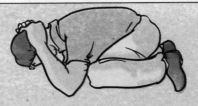

Fig. 8.15 Protecting from a tornado

"I saw the cloud coming and tried to take shelter inside. But as soon as I reached for the doorknob, the house took off into the sky. I was not hurt at all."

"After the storm we had to clean the debris from the wheat fields. We picked up splintered boards and tree branches as well as dead chickens with their feathers blown off and rabbits looked like they had been skinned."

A tornado shelter is a room situated deep inside or underground having no windows. Or otherwise it is better to shut windows and take shelter under a table, workbench, where debris cannot reach. One has to bow down on knees protecting head and neck using arms (Fig. 8.15).

Tornadoes: In our country they are not very frequent. A tornado is a dark funnel shaped cloud that reaches from the sky to the ground (Fig. 8.16). Most of the tornadoes are weak. A violent tornado can travel at speeds of about 300 km/h. Tornadoes may form within cyclones.

The whole coastline of India is vulnerable to cyclones, particularly the east coast. The west coast of India is less vulnerable to cyclonic storms both in terms of intensity and frequency of the cyclones.

8.7 Effective Safety Measures

- A cyclone forecast and warning service.
- Rapid communication of warnings to the

Fig. 8.16 *Image of a tornado*
[National Severe Storm Laboratory (NSSL)]
Courtesy: India Meteorological Department,
New Delhi

We have learnt that all storms are low-pressure systems. Wind speed plays an important role in the formation of storms. It is, therefore, important to measure the wind speed. The instrument that measures the wind speed is called an anemometer.

Fig. 8.17 *An anemometer for measuring the speed of wind*

Courtesy: India Meteorological Department,
New Delhi

Government agencies, the ports, fishermen, ships and to the general public.

- Construction of cyclone shelters in the cyclone prone areas, and Administrative arrangements for moving people fast to safer places.

Action on the part of the people

- We should not ignore the warnings issued by the meteorological department through TV, radio, or newspapers.
- We should —
  make necessary arrangements to shift the essential household goods, domestic animals and vehicles, etc. to safer places;
  avoid driving on roads through standing water, as floods may have damaged the roads; and
  keep ready the phone numbers of all emergency services like police, fire brigade, and medical centres.

Some other precautions, if you are staying in a cyclone hit area —

- Do not drink water that could be contaminated. Always store drinking water for emergencies.
- Do not touch wet switches and fallen power lines.
- Do not go out just for the sake of fun.
- Do not pressurise the rescue force by making undue demands.
- Cooperate and help your neighbours and friends.

8.8 ADVANCED TECHNOLOGY HAS HELPED

These days we are better protected. In the early part of the last century, coastal residents may have had less than a day to prepare or evacuate their homes from an oncoming cyclone. The world today is very different. Thanks to satellites and radars, a **Cyclone alert** or **Cyclone watch** is issued 48 hours in advance of any expected storm and a **Cyclone warning** is issued 24 hrs in advance. The message is broadcast every hour or half hour when a cyclone is nearer the coast. Several national and international organisations cooperate to monitor the cyclone-related disasters.

Keywords

Anemometer	Low pressure	Tornado
Cyclone	Monsoon winds	Typhoon
Hurricane	Pressure	Wind flow pattern
Lightning	Thunderstorms	

What you have learnt

- Air around us exerts pressure.
- Air expands on heating and contracts on cooling.
- Warm air rises up, whereas comparatively cooler air tends to sink towards the earth's surface.
- As warm air rises, air pressure at that place is reduced and the cooler air moves to that place.
- The moving air is called wind.
- Uneven heating on the earth is the main cause of wind movements.
- Winds carrying water vapour bring rain.
- High-speed winds and air pressure difference can cause cyclones.
- It has become easier to monitor cyclones with the help of advance technology like satellites and radars.
- Self-help is the best help. Therefore it is better to plan in advance and be ready with defence against any approaching cyclone.
- The following flow chart will help you to understand the phenomena that lead to the formation of clouds and falling of rain and creation of storms and cyclones:

Difference of temperature between two regions
▼
Sets convection in air
▼
Warm air rises, creating a low-pressure area
▼
Cool air converges to the low-pressure area
▼
Warm air rises, cools and the water vapour condenses to form clouds
▼
The bigger water drops in the cloud fall to the ground as rain, hail or snow
▼
Falling water droplets and rising air move vigorously to produce thunderstorm
▼
Under certain weather condition storms may develop into cyclones

Exercises

1. Fill the missing word in the blank spaces in the following statements:

   (a) Wind is_____air.

   (b) Winds are generated due to_____heating on the earth.

   (c) Near the earth's surface _____air rises up whereas _____ air comes down.

   (d) Air moves from a region of _____ pressure to a region of_____ pressure.

2. Suggest two methods to find out wind direction at a given place.

3. State two experiences that made you think that air exerts pressure (other than those given in the text).

4. You want to buy a house. Would you like to buy a house having windows but no ventilators? Explain your answer.

5. Explain why holes are made in hanging banners and hoardings.

6. How will you help your neighbours in case cyclone approaches your village/town?

7. What planning is required in advance to deal with the situation created by a cyclone?

8. Which one of the following place is unlikely to be affected by a cyclone.

   (i) Chennai   (ii)   Mangaluru (Mangalore)

   (iii)   Amritsar   (iv)   Puri

9. Which of the statements given below is correct?

   (i)   In winter the winds flow from the land to the ocean.

   (ii)   In summer the winds flow from the land towards the ocean.

   (iii)   A cyclone is formed by a very high-pressure system with very high-speed winds revolving around it.

   (iv)   The coastline of India is not vulnerable to cyclones.

Extended Learning — Activities and Projects

1. You can perform the Activity 8.5 in the chapter slight differently at home. Use two plastic bottles of the same size. Stretch one balloon on the neck of each bottle. Keep one bottle in the sun and the other in the shade. Record your observations. Compare these observations and the result with those of Activity 8.5.

2. You can make your own anemometer.

Collect the following items:

4 small paper cups (used ice cream cups), 2 strips of cardboard (20cm long and 2cm wide), gum, stapler, a sketch pen and a sharpened pencil with eraser at one end.

Take a scale; draw crosses on the cardboard strips as shown in the Fig. 8.18. This will give you the centres of the strips.

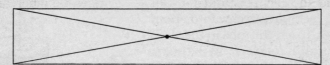

Fig. 8.18 *Finding centre of the strips*

Fig. 8.19 *A model of an anemometer*

Fix the strips at the centre, putting one over the other so that they make a plus (+) sign. Now fix the cups at the ends of the strips. Colour the outer surface of one cup with a marker or a sketch pen. All the 4 cups should face in the same direction.

Push a pin through the centre of the strips and attach the strips and the cups to the eraser of the pencil. Check that the strips rotate freely when you blow on the cups. Your anemometer is ready. Counting the number of rotations per minute will give you an estimate of the speed of the wind. To observe the changes in the wind speed, use it at different places and different times of the day.

If you do not have a pencil with attached eraser you can use the tip of a ball pen. The only condition is that the strips should rotate freely.

Remember that this anemometer will indicate only speed changes. It will not give you the actual wind speed.

3. Collect articles and photographs from newspapers and magazines about storms and cyclones. Make a story on the basis of what you learnt in this chapter and the matter collected by you.

4. Suppose you are a member of a committee, which is responsible for creating **development plan** of a coastal state. Prepare a short speech indicating the measures to be taken to reduce the suffering of the people caused by cyclones.

5. Interview eyewitness to collect the actual experience of people affected by a cyclone.

6. Take an aluminium tube about 15 cm long and 1 to 1.5 cm in diameter. Cut slice of a medium-sized potato about 2 cm thick. Insert the tube in the slice, press it, and rotate it 2–3 times. Remove the tube. You will find a piece of potato fixed in the tube like a piston head. Repeat the same process with the other end of the tube. Now you have the tube with both ends closed by potato pieces with an air column in between. Take a pencil with one end unsharpened. Place this end at one of the pieces of potato. Press it suddenly to push the potato piece in the tube. Observe what happens. The activity shows rather dramatically how increased air pressure can push things.

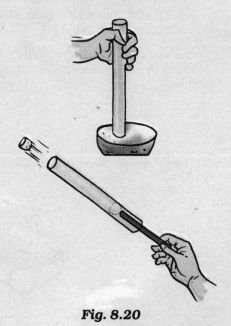

Fig. 8.20

CAUTION: When you perform this activity, make sure that nobody is standing in front of the tube.

You can read more on the related topics on the following websites:

http://www.imd.gov.in/

http://library.thinkquest.org/10136/

www.bom.gov.au/lam/students_teachers/cycmod.shtml

www.chunder.com/ski/lightanim.html

Did you know?

A bolt of lightning travels at a speed of more than 400,000 km/h. It can heat the air around it to a temperature which is more than 4 times the temperature of the surface of the sun. That is what makes lightning so dangerous.

9 Soil

Soil is one of the most important natural resources. It supports the growth of plants by holding the roots firmly and supplying water and nutrients. It is the home for many organisms. Soil is essential for agriculture. Agriculture provides food, clothing and shelter for all. Soil is thus an inseparable part of our life. The earthy fragrance of soil after the first rain is always refreshing.

9.1 SOIL TEEMING WITH LIFE

One day during the rainy season Paheli and Boojho observed an earthworm coming out of the soil. Paheli wondered whether there were other organisms also in the soil. Let us find out.

Activity 9.1

Collect some soil samples and observe them carefully. You can use a hand lens. Examine each sample carefully and fill in Table 9.1.

▪ Discuss your observations with your friends.

▪ Are the soil samples collected by your friends similar to the ones collected by you?

Boojho and Paheli have used soil in many ways. They enjoy playing with it. It is a great fun indeed.

Make a list of the uses of soil.

Fig. 9.1 *Children playing with soil*

Table 9.1

S. No.	Soil source	Plants	Animals	Any other observations
1.	Garden soil	Grass, ...	Ant, ...	
2.	Soil from the roadside	....		
3.	Soil from the area where construction is going on	....		
4.		....	....	
5.		....	....	

I wonder why I found some pieces of plastic articles and polythene bags in the soil sample collected from the roadside and the garden.

Polythene bags and plastics pollute the soil. They also kill the organisms living in the soil. That is why there is a demand to ban the polythene bags and plastics. Other substances which pollute the soil are a number of waste products, chemicals and pesticides. Waste products and chemicals should be treated before they are released into the soil. The use of pesticides should be minimised.

I want to know whether the soil from a field can be used to make toys?

9.2 Soil Profile

Soil is composed of distinct layers. Perform the following activity to find out how these layers are arranged.

Activity 9.2

Take a little soil. Break the clumps with your hand to powder it. Now take a glass tumbler, three quarters filled with water,

and then add a handful of soil to it. Stir it well with a stick to dissolve the soil. Now let it stand undisturbed for some time (Fig. 9.2). Afterwards, observe it and answer the following questions:

Fig. 9.2 *Layers of soil*

- Do you see layers of particles of different sizes in the glass tumbler?
- Draw a diagram showing these layers.
- Are there some dead rotting leaves or animal remains floating on water? The rotting dead matter in the soil is called **humus**.

You probably know that the soil is formed by the breaking down of rocks by the action of wind, water and climate. This process is called **weathering**. The nature of any soil depends upon the rocks from which it has been formed and the type of vegetation that grows in it.

A vertical section through different layers of the soil is called the **soil profile**. Each layer differs in feel (texture), colour, depth and chemical composition. These layers are referred to as **horizons** (Fig. 9.3).

soil fertile and provides nutrients to growing plants. This layer is generally soft, porous and can retain more water. It is called the **topsoil** or the **A-horizon**.

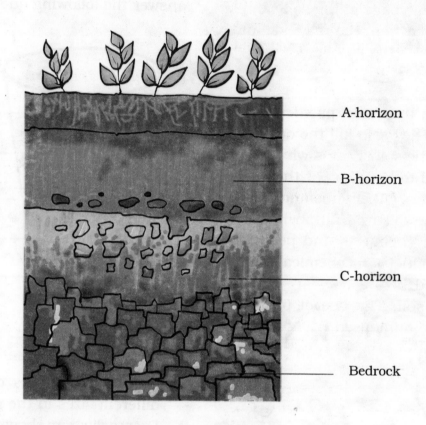

— A-horizon

— B-horizon

— C-horizon

Bedrock

Fig. 9.3 *Soil profile*

We usually see the top surface of the soil, not the layers below it. If we look at the sides of a recently dug ditch, we can see the inner layers of the soil, too. Such a view enables us to observe the soil profile at that place. Soil profile can also be seen while digging a well or laying the foundation of a building. It can also be seen at the sides of a road on a hill or at a steep river bank.

The uppermost horizon is generally dark in colour as it is rich in humus and minerals. The humus makes the

This provides shelter for many living organisms such as worms, rodents, moles and beetles. The roots of small plants are embedded entirely in the topsoil.

The next layer has a lesser amount of humus but more of minerals. This layer is generally harder and more compact and is called the **B-horizon** or the middle layer.

The third layer is the **C-horizon**, which is made up of small lumps of rocks with cracks and crevices. Below this layer is the **bedrock**, which is hard and difficult to dig with a spade.

9.3 Soil Types

As you know, weathering of rocks produces small particles of various materials. These include sand and clay. The relative amount of sand and clay depends upon the rock from which the particles were formed, that is the parent rock. **The mixture of rock particles and humus is called the soil**. Living organisms, such as bacteria, plant roots and earthworm are also important parts of any soil.

The soil is classified on the basis of the proportion of particles of various sizes. If soil contains greater proportion of big particles it is called **sandy soil**. If the proportion of fine particles is relatively higher, then it is called **clayey soil**. If the amount of large and fine particles is about the same, then the soil is called **loamy**. Thus, the soil can be classified as sandy, clayey and loamy.

The sizes of the particles in a soil have a very important influence on its properties. Sand particles are quite large. They cannot fit closely together, so there are large spaces between them. These spaces are filled with air. We say that the sand is well aerated. Water can drain quickly through the spaces between the sand particles. So, sandy soils tend to be light, well aerated and rather dry. Clay particles, being much smaller, pack tightly together, leaving little space for air. Unlike sandy soil,

water can be held in the tiny gaps between the particles of clay. So clay soils have little air. But they are heavy as they hold more water than the sandy soils.

The best topsoil for growing plants is loam. **Loamy soil** is a mixture of sand, clay and another type of soil particle known as silt. Silt occurs as a deposit in river beds. The size of the silt particles is between those of sand and clay. The loamy soil also has humus in it. It has the right water holding capacity for the growth of plants.

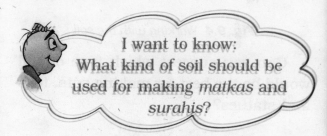

I want to know:
What kind of soil should be used for making *matkas* and *surahis*?

Activity 9.3

Collect samples of clayey, loamy and sandy soils. Take a fistful of soil from one of the samples. Remove any pebbles, rocks or grass blades from it. Now add water drop by drop and knead the soil [Fig. 9.4 (a)]. Add just enough water so that a ball [Fig. 9.4 (b)] can be made from it, but at the same time it should not be sticky. Try to make a ball [Fig. 9.4 (c)] from this soil. On a flat surface, roll this ball into a cylinder [Fig. 9.4 (d)]. Try to make a ring from this cylinder [Fig. 9.4 (e)]. Repeat this activity with other samples also. Does the extent to which a soil can be shaped indicate its type?

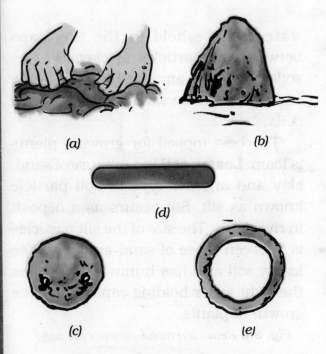

(a)   (b)

(d)

(c)   (e)

Fig. 9.4 *Working with the soil*

Can you suggest which type of soil would be the best for making pots, toys and statues?

9.4 Properties of Soil

You have listed some uses of soil. Let us perform some activities to find the characteristics of the soil.

Percolation rate of water in soil

Boojho and Paheli marked two different squares of 50 cm × 50 cm each, one on the floor of their house and the other on the *kutcha* (unpaved) road. They filled two bottles of the same size with water. They emptied the water from the bottles, one each, at the same time in the two squares. They observed that the water on the floor flowed down and was not absorbed. On the *kutcha* road, on the other hand, the water was absorbed.

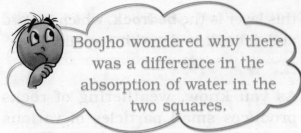

Boojho wondered why there was a difference in the absorption of water in the two squares.

Now let us perform an activity to understand this.

Activity 9.4

For this activity divide yourself into three teams. Name the teams A, B and C. You will be finding out how fast the water passes down the soil. You will need a hollow cylinder or a pipe. Ensure that each team uses pipes of the same diameter. Some suggestions for obtaining such a pipe are given below:

1. If possible, get a small tin can and cut off its bottom.

2. If PVC pipe (approx. diameter 5 cm) is available, cut it into 20 cm long pieces and use them.

At the place where you collect the soil, place the pipe about 2 cm deep in the ground. Pour 200 mL water in the pipe slowly. For measuring 200 mL water you can use any empty 200 mL bottle. Note

Fig. 9.5 *Measuring rate of percolation*

the time when you start pouring water. When all the water has percolated leaving the pipe empty, note the time again. Be careful not to let the water spill over or run down on the outside of the pipe while pouring. Calculate the rate of percolation by using the following formula:

$$\text{percolation rate (mL/min)} = \frac{\text{amount of water (mL)}}{\text{percolation time (min)}}$$

For example, suppose that for a certain sample, it took 20 minutes for 200 mL to percolate. So,

$$\text{rate of percolation} = \frac{200 \text{ mL}}{20 \text{ min}} = 10 \text{ mL/min}$$

Calculate the rate of percolation in your soil sample. Compare your findings with others and arrange the soil samples in the increasing order of the rate of percolation.

9.5 MOISTURE IN SOIL

Have you ever passed through a farmland during a hot summer day? Perhaps you noticed that the air above the land is shimmering. Why is it so? Try out this activity and find the answer.

Activity 9.5

Take a boiling tube. Put two spoonfulls of a soil sample in it. Heat it on a flame (Fig. 9.6) and observe it. Let us find out what happens upon heating.

Do you see water drops any where? If yes, where did you find them?

On heating, water in the soil evaporates, moves up and condenses on the cooler inner walls of the upper part of the boiling tube.

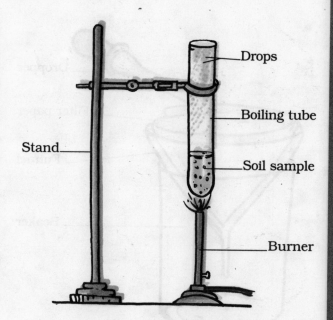

Fig. 9.6 Removing moisture from the soil

On a hot summer day, the vapour coming out of the soil reflect the sunlight and the air above the soil seems to shimmer.

After heating the soil, take it out of the tube. Compare it with the soil which has not been heated. Note the difference between the two.

9.6 ABSORPTION OF WATER BY SOIL

Do all the soils absorb water to the same extent? Let us find out.

Activity 9.6

Take a plastic funnel. Take a filter paper (or a piece of newspaper sheet), fold and place it as shown in the figure. Weigh 50g of dry, powdered soil and pour it into the funnel. Measure a certain amount of water in a measuring cylinder and pour it drop by drop on the soil. You can use a dropper for this purpose. Do not let all the water fall at one spot.

- Dropper
- Filter paper
- Funnel
- Beaker

Fig. 9.7 *Absorption of water in the soil*

Pour water all over the soil. Keep pouring water till it starts dripping. Subtract the amount of water left in the measuring cylinder from the amount you started with. This is the amount of water retained by the soil. Record your results in your notebook in the following manner:

Weight of soil = 50g

Initial volume of water in the measuring cylinder = U mL

Final volume of water in the measuring cylinder = V mL

Volume of water absorbed by the soil = (U – V) mL

Weight of water absorbed by the soil = (U – V) g

(1 mL of water has weight equal to 1 g)

percentage of water absorbed

$$= \frac{(U - V)}{50} \times 100$$

Repeat this activity with different soil samples. Would you get the same results for all the samples? Discuss the results with your friends and answer the following question:

- Which soil would have the highest percolation rate?
- Which soil would have the lowest percolation rate?
- Boojho heard from his neighbourer that 8–10 days after the rain, the level of water in a pond or well rises. Which type of soil will allow water to reach a well faster and in greater amount?
- Which type of soil retains the highest amount of water and which retains the least?
- Can you suggest any method to let more rain water percolate and reach the water underground?

9.7 Soil and Crops

Different types of soils are found in different parts of India. In some parts there is clayey soil, in some parts there is loamy soil while in some other parts there is sandy soil.

Soil is affected by wind, rainfall, temperature, light and humidity. These are some important climatic factors which affect the soil profile and bring changes in the soil structure. The

Gram (g) and kilogram (kg) are actually units of mass. A mass of 1 gram weighs 1 gram weight, and a mass of 1 kilogram weighs 1 kilogram weight. However, in daily life, and in commerce and industry, the distinction between gram and gram weight is generally omitted.

climatic factors, as well as the components of soil, determine the various types of vegetation and crops that might grow in any region.

Clayey and loamy soils are both suitable for growing cereals like wheat, and gram. Such soils are good at retaining water. For paddy, soils rich in clay and organic matter and having a good capacity to retain water are ideal. For lentils (*masoor*) and other pulses, loamy soils, which drain water easily, are required. For cotton, sandy-loam or loam, which drain water easily

A case study

John, Rashida and Radha went to Leeladhar Dada and Sontosh Malviya of Sohagpur in Madhya Pradesh. Leeladhar Dada was preparing the soil to make items like *surahi*, *matki*, *kalla* (earthen frying pan) etc. The following is the conversation they all had with Leeladhar Dada:

– Where was the soil obtained from?

Dada–We brought the black soil from a piece of barren land.

– How is the soil prepared?

Dada–Dry soil will be placed in a large tank and would be cleaned of pebbles etc. After removing these things the soil will be soaked for around 8 hours. This soil would be kneaded after mixing horse dung. The kneaded soil would be placed on the wheel and given appropriate shape. The final shape is given with hands. The items are coloured after three days of drying. All the items are baked at high temperature after drying in the air.

– Why is the horse dung mixed in soil?

Dada–Burnt horse dung helps open up the pores in the soil. So that water could percolate out of the *matkas* and *surahis*, evaporate and cools the water inside. You know Sohagpuri *surahis* and *matkas* are famous in far off places like Jabalpur, Nagpur, Allahabad, etc.

Fig. 9.8 Making pots

and can hold plenty of air, are more suitable.

Crops such as wheat are grown in the fine clayey soils, because they are rich in humus and are very fertile. Find from your teachers, parents and farmers the type of soils and crops grown in your area. Enter the data in the following Table 9.2:

Which kind of soil would be most suitable for planting rice? Soil with a higher or lower rate of percolation?

What is the difference between rate of percolation and the amount of water retained? Boojho, you seem to have forgotten what you read earlier. Go and reread the lesson again and you will find the answer.

Table 9.2

S. No.	Type of soil	Crop grown
1.	Clayey	Wheat ....
2.		
3.		

Keywords

Clayey	Moisture
Humus	Sandy
Loamy	Water retention
Percolation	

Soil erosion

The removal of land surface by water, wind or ice is known as erosion. Plant roots firmly bind the soil. In the absence of plants, soil becomes loose. So it can be moved by wind and flowing water. Erosion of soil is more severe in areas of little or no surface vegetation, such as desert or bare lands. So, cutting of trees and deforestation should be prevented and effort should be made to increase the green areas.

What you have learnt

- Soil is important for life on the earth.
- Soil profile is a section through different layers of the soil, Various layers are called horizons.
- Soil is of different types: clayey, loamy and sandy.
- Percolation rate of water is different in different types of soil. It is highest in the sandy soil and least in the clayey soil.
- Different types of soils are used to cultivate different types of crops. Clay and loam are suitable for growing wheat, gram and paddy. Cotton is grown in sandy loam soil.

- Soil holds water in it, which is called soil moisture. The capacity of a soil to hold water is important for various crops.
- Clayey soil is used to make pots, toys and statues.

Exercises

Tick the most suitable answer in questions 1 and 2.

1. In addition to the rock particles, the soil contains
   - (i)   air and water
   - (ii) water and plants
   - (iii) minerals, organic matter, air and water
   - (iv) water, air and plants

2. The water holding capacity is the highest in
   - (i)   sandy soil
   - (ii) clayey soil
   - (iii) loamy soil
   - (iv) mixture of sand and loam

3. Match the items in Column I with those in Column II:

Column I		Column II	
(i)	A home for living organisms	(a)	Large particles
(ii)	Upper layer of the soil	(b)	All kinds of soil
(iii)	Sandy soil	(c)	Dark in colour
(iv)	Middle layer of the soil	(d)	Small particles and packed tight
(v)	Clayey soil	(e)	Lesser amount of humus

4. Explain how soil is formed.

5. How is clayey soil useful for crops?

6. List the differences between clayey soil and sandy soil.

7. Sketch the cross section of soil and label the various layers.

8. Razia conducted an experiment in the field related to the rate of percolation. She observed that it took 40 min for 200 mL of water to percolate through the soil sample. Calculate the rate of percolation.

9. Explain how soil pollution and soil erosion could be prevented.

10. Solve the following crossword puzzle with the clues given:

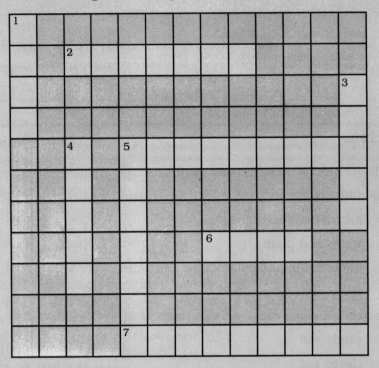

Across

2. Plantation prevents it.

5. Use should be banned to avoid soil pollution.

6. Type of soil used for making pottery.

7. Living organism in the soil.

Down

1. In desert soil erosion occurs through.

3. Clay and loam are suitable for cereals like.

4. This type of soil can hold very little water.

5. Collective name for layers of soil.

Extended Learning — Activities and Projects

1. Boojho would like to know the difference between raw and baked soil? Investigate how the soil from which *matkas* are made is different from the soil used to make statues.

2. Paheli is worried. She could see a brick kiln from her house. Bricks were being made there. There was so much smoke coming out of the kiln. She was told that the best quality of clay is required for making pottery, statues and bricks. She has seen truck loads of bricks being taken away for construction of buildings. At this rate, she fears, no soil will be left. Are her fears justified? Discuss this problem with your parents, teachers and other experts of your area and prepare a report.

3. Try to find out the moisture content of a soil sample. One method is given here.

Activity: Take 100g soil. (Take help from any shopkeepers to weigh the soil.) Place it on a newspaper in the sun and allow it to dry for two hours. This activity is best done in the afternoon. Take care that the soil does not spill outside the newspaper. After drying it, weigh the soil again. The difference in the weight of the soil before and after drying gives you the amount of moisture contained in 100 g of soil. This is called the percentage moisture content.

Suppose your sample of soil loses 10 g on drying. Then

$$\text{Per cent of moisture in soil} = \frac{\text{wt. of moisture (g)}}{\text{Original wt. of soil sample (g)}} \times 100$$

In this example

$$\text{Per cent of moisture in soil} = \frac{10 \times 100}{100} = 10\%$$

Did you know?

Rivers of north India, which flow from Himalayas, bring a variety of materials including silt, clay, sand and gravel. They deposit their materials called alluvial soil, in the planes of north India. This soil is very fertile and supports nearby half the population of India.

10 Respiration in Organisms

One day Boojho was eagerly waiting to meet his grandparents who were coming to the town after a year. He was in a real hurry as he wanted to receive them at the bus-stop. He ran fast and reached the bus-stop in a few minutes. He was breathing rapidly. His grandmother asked him why he was breathing so fast. Boojho told her that he came running all the way. But the question got stuck in his mind. He wondered why running makes a person breathe faster. The answer to Boojho's question lies in understanding why we breathe. Breathing is a part of respiration. Let us learn about respiration.

10.1 Why do We Respire?

In Chapter 2 you learnt that all organisms are made of small microscopic units called cells. A cell is the smallest structural and functional unit of an organism. Each cell of an organism performs certain functions such as nutrition, transport, excretion and reproduction. To perform these functions, the cell needs energy. Even when we are eating, sleeping or reading we require energy. But, where does this energy come from? Can you say why your parents insist that you should eat regularly? The food has stored energy, which is released during respiration.

Therefore, all living organisms respire to get energy from food. During breathing, we breathe in air. You know that air contains oxygen. We breathe out air which is rich in carbon dioxide. The air we breathe in is transported to all parts of the body and ultimately to each cell. In the cells, oxygen in the air helps in the breakdown of food. The process of breakdown of food in the cell with the release of energy is called **cellular respiration**. Cellular respiration takes place in the **cells of all organisms**.

In the cell, the food (glucose) is broken down into carbon dioxide and water using oxygen. When breakdown of glucose occurs with the use of oxygen it is called **aerobic respiration**. Food can also be broken down, without using oxygen. This is called **anaerobic respiration**. Breakdown of food releases energy.

Glucose $\xrightarrow{\text{With the use of oxygen}}$ carbon dioxide + water + energy

You should know that there are some organisms such as yeast that can survive in the absence of air. They are called **anaerobes**. They get energy through anaerobic respiration. In the absence of oxygen, glucose breaks down into alcohol and carbon dioxide, as given below:

Glucose $\xrightarrow{\text{Without the use of oxygen}}$ alcohol + carbon dioxide + energy

Yeasts are single-celled organisms. They respire anaerobically and during this process yield alcohol. They are, therefore, used to make wine and beer.

Our muscle cells can also respire anaerobically, but only for a short time, when there is a temporary deficiency of oxygen. During heavy exercise, fast running (Fig. 10.1), cycling, walking for many hours or heavy weight lifting, the demand for energy is high. But the supply of oxygen to produce the energy is limited. Then anaerobic respiration takes places in the muscle cells to fulfil the demand of energy:

$$\text{Glucose} \xrightarrow{\text{in the absence of oxygen}}$$
(in muscle)

lactic acid + energy

Fig. 10.1 *During exercise, some muscles may respire anaerobically*

Have you ever wondered why you get muscle cramps after heavy exercise? The cramps occur when muscle cells respire anaerobically. The partial breakdown of glucose produces lactic acid. The accumulation of lactic acid causes muscle cramps. We get relief from cramps after a hot water bath or a massage. Can you guess why it is so? Hot water bath or massage improves circulation of blood. As a result, the supply of oxygen to the muscle cells increases. The increase in the supply of oxygen results in the complete breakdown of lactic acid into carbon dioxide and water.

10.2 Breathing

Activity 10.1

CAUTION
Do this activity under the supervision of your teacher.

Close your nostrils and mouth tightly and look at a watch. What did you feel after some time? How long were you able to keep both of them closed? Note down the time for which you could hold your breath (Fig. 10.2).

So, now you know that you cannot survive for long without breathing.

Breathing means taking in air rich in oxygen and giving out air rich in carbon dioxide with the help of respiratory organs. The taking in of air rich in oxygen into the body is called **inhalation** and giving out of air rich in carbon dioxide is known as **exhalation**. It is a continuous process which goes on all the time and throughout the life of an organism.

The number of times a person breathes in a minute is termed as the **breathing rate**. During breathing inhalation and exhalation take place alternately. A breath means one inhalation plus one exhalation. Would

Fig. 10.2 *Holding breath*

Boojho noticed that when he released his breath after holding it for some time, he had to breathe heavily. Can you tell him why it was so?

you like to find out your breathing rate? Do you want to know whether it is constant or it changes according to the requirement of oxygen by the body? Let us find out by doing the following activity.

Activity 10.2

Generally we are not aware that we are breathing. However, if you try you can count your rate of breathing. Breathe in and out normally. Find out how many times you breathe in and breathe out in a minute? Did you inhale the same number of times as you exhaled? Now count your breathing rate (number of breaths/minute) after brisk walk and after running. Record your breathing rate as soon as you finish and also after complete rest. Tabulate your findings and compare your breathing rates under different conditions with those of your classmates.

From the above activity, you must have realised that whenever a person needs extra energy, he/she breathes faster. As a result more oxygen is

Table 10.1 Changes in breathing rate under different conditions

Name of the classmate	Breathing rate			
	Normal	After a brisk walk for 10 minutes	After running fast 100 m	At rest
Self				

On an average, an adult human being at rest breathes in and out 15–18 times in a minute. During heavy exercise, the breathing rate can increase upto 25 times per minute. While we exercise, not only do we breathe fast, we also take deep breaths and thus inhale more oxygen.

supplied to our cells. It speeds up the breakdown of food and more energy is released. Does this explain why do we feel hungry after a physical activity?

When you feel drowsy, does your breathing rate slow down? Does your body receive sufficient oxygen?

Activity 10.3

Figure 10.3 shows the various activities carried out by a person during a normal

Fig. 10.3 *Variation in the breathing rate during different activities*

Paheli wants to know why we yawn when we are sleepy or drowsy.

day. Can you say in which activity, the rate of breathing will be the slowest and in which it will be the fastest? Assign numbers to the pictures in the order of increasing rate of breathing according to your experience.

10.3 HOW DO WE BREATHE?

Let us now learn about the mechanism of breathing. Normally we take in air through our nostrils. When we inhale air, it passes through our nostrils into the **nasal cavity**. From the nasal cavity, the air reaches our **lungs** through the windpipe. Lungs are present in the **chest cavity** (Fig. 10.4). This cavity is surrounded by ribs on the sides. A large, muscular sheet called **diaphragm** forms the floor of the chest cavity (Fig. 10.4). Breathing involves the movement of the diaphragm and the rib cage.

During inhalation, ribs move up and outwards and diaphragm moves down. This movement increases space in our chest cavity and air rushes into the lungs. The lungs get filled with air. During exhalation, ribs move down and inwards, while diaphragm moves up to its former position. This reduces the size of the chest cavity and air is pushed out of the lungs (Fig. 10.5). These movements in our body can be felt easily. Take a deep breath. Keep your palm on the abdomen, feel the movement of abdomen. What do you find?

After having learnt that during breathing there are changes in the size of the chest cavity, children got involved in the chest expansion competition.

Smoking damages lungs. Smoking is also linked to cancer. It must be avoided.

Everyone was boasting that she/he could expand it the maximum. How about doing this activity in the class with your classmates?

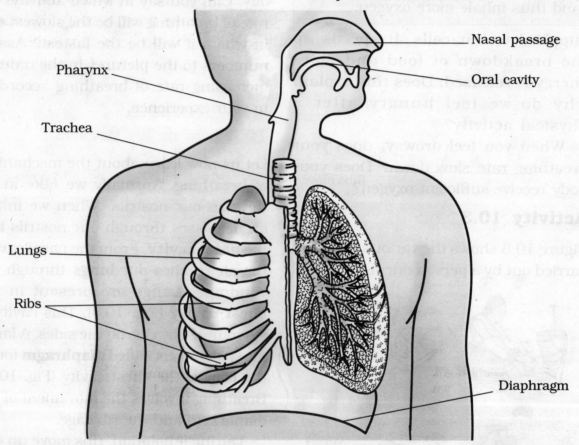

Nasal passage

Oral cavity

Pharynx

Trachea

Lungs

Ribs

Diaphragm

Fig 10.4 Human respiratory system

The air around us has various types of unwanted particles, such as smoke, dust, pollens, etc. When we inhale, the particles get trapped in the hair present in our nasal cavity. However, sometimes these particles may get past the hair in the nasal cavity. Then they irritate the lining of the cavity, as a result of which we sneeze. Sneezing expels these foreign particles from the inhaled air and a dust-free, clean air enters our body.

TAKE CARE: When you sneeze, you should cover your nose so that the foreign particles you expel are not inhaled by other persons.

Activity 10.4

Take a deep breath. Measure the size of the chest with a measuring tape (Fig. 10.6) and record your observations in Table 10.2. Measure the size of the chest again when expanded and indicate which classmate shows the maximum expansion of the chest.

We can understand the mechanism of breathing by a simple model.

Activity 10.5

Take a wide plastic bottle. Remove the bottom. Get a Y-shaped glass or plastic tube. Make a hole in the lid so that the tube may pass through it. To the forked end of the tube fix two deflated balloons. Introduce the tube into the bottle as shown in Fig. 10.7. Now cap the bottle. Seal it to make it airtight. To the open base of the bottle tie a thin rubber or plastic sheet using a large rubber band.

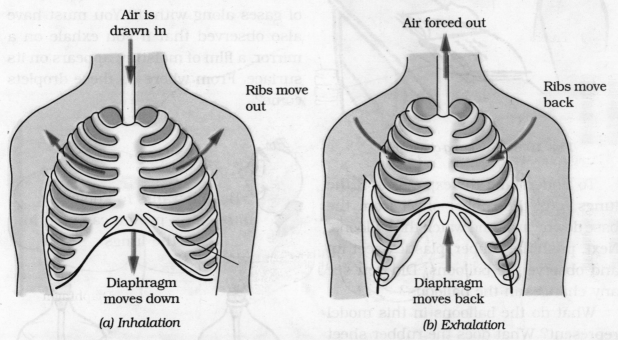

Fig. 10.5 *Mechanism of breathing in human beings*

Table 10.2: Effect of breathing on the chest size of some classmates

Name of the classmate	Size of the chest (cm)		
	During inhalation	During exhalation	Difference in size

Fig. 10.6 *Measuring chest size*

To understand the expansion of the lungs, pull the rubber sheet from the base downwards and watch the balloons. Next, push the rubber/plastic sheet up and observe the balloons. Did you see any changes in the balloons?

What do the balloons in this model represent? What does the rubber sheet represent?

Now, you should be able to explain the mechanism of breathing.

10.4 WHAT DO WE BREATHE OUT ?

Activity 10.6

Take a slender, clean test tube or a glass/plastic bottle. Make a hole in its lid and fix it on the bottle. Pour some freshly prepared lime water in the test-tube. Insert a plastic straw through the hole in the lid in such a way that it dips in lime water. Now blow gently through the straw a few times (Fig. 10.8). Is there a change in the appearance of lime water? Can you explain this change on the basis of what you learnt in Chapter 6?

You are aware that air we inhale or exhale is a mixture of gases. What do we exhale? Do we exhale only carbon dioxide or a mixture of gases along with it? You must have also observed that if you exhale on a mirror, a film of moisture appears on its surface. From where do these droplets come?

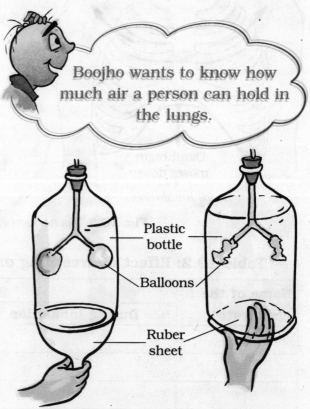

Boojho wants to know how much air a person can hold in the lungs.

Fig 10.7 *Model to show mechanism of breathing*

Plastic bottle

Balloons

Ruber sheet

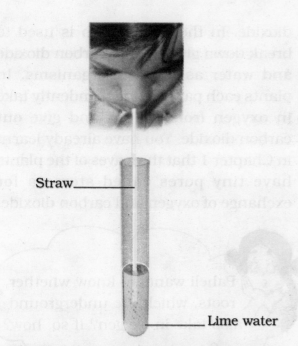

Straw

Lime water

Fig 10.8 *Effect of exhaled air on lime water*

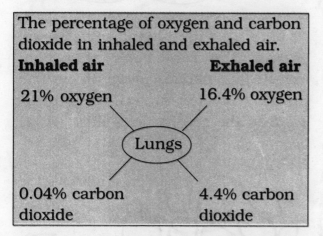

The percentage of oxygen and carbon dioxide in inhaled and exhaled air.

Inhaled air	Exhaled air
21% oxygen	16.4% oxygen
0.04% carbon dioxide	4.4% carbon dioxide

Lungs

10.5 BREATHING IN OTHER ANIMALS

Animals such as elephants, lions, cows, goats, frogs, lizards, snakes, birds, have lungs in their chest cavities like the human beings.

How do other organisms breathe? Do they also have lungs like those of human beings? Let us find out.

Cockroach: A cockroach has small openings on the sides of its body. Other insects also have similar openings.

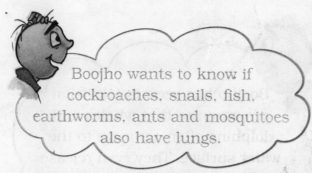

Boojho wants to know if cockroaches, snails, fish, earthworms, ants and mosquitoes also have lungs.

These openings are called **spiracles** (Fig. 10.9). Insects have a network of air tubes called **tracheae** for gas exchange. Oxygen rich air rushes through spiracles into the tracheal tubes, diffuses into the body tissue, and reaches every cell of the body. Similarly, carbon dioxide from the cells goes into the tracheal tubes and moves out through spiracles. These air tubes or tracheae are found only in insects and not in any other group of animals.

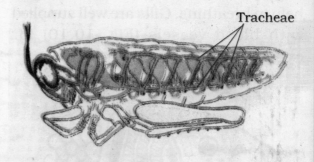

Tracheae

Fig.10.9 *Tracheal system*

Earthworm: Recall from Chapter 9 of Class VI that earthworms breathe through their skins. The skin of an earthworm feels moist and slimy on touching. Gases can easily pass through them. Though frogs have a pair of lungs like human beings, they can also breathe through their skin, which is moist and slippery.

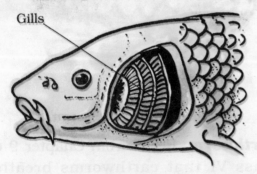

Boojho has seen in television programmes that whales and dolphins often come up to the water surface. They even release a fountain of water sometimes while moving upwards. Why do they do so?

10.6 BREATHING UNDER WATER

Can we breathe and survive in water? There are many organisms which live in water. How do they breathe under water?

You have studied in Class VI that gills in fish help them to use oxygen dissolved in water. Gills are projections of the skin. You may wonder how gills help in breathing. Gills are well supplied with blood vessels (Fig. 10.10) for exchange of gases.

Gills

Fig. 10.10 *Breathing organs in fish*

10.7 DO PLANTS ALSO RESPIRE?

Like other living organisms, plants also respire for their survival as you have learnt in Class VI. They also take in oxygen from the air and give out carbon

dioxide. In the cells oxygen is used to break down glucose into carbon dioxide and water as in other organisms. In plants each part can independently take in oxygen from the air and give out carbon dioxide. You have already learnt in Chapter 1 that the leaves of the plants have tiny pores called stomata for exchange of oxygen and carbon dioxide.

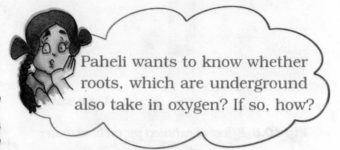

Paheli wants to know whether roots, which are underground also take in oxygen? If so, how?

Like all other living cells of the plants, the root cells also need oxygen to generate energy. Roots take up air from the air spaces present between the soil particles (Fig. 10.11).

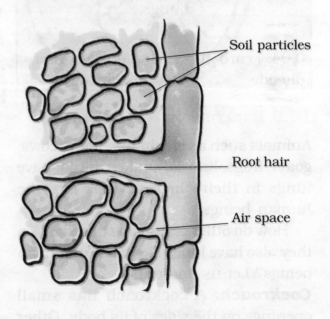

Soil particles

Root hair

Air space

Fig. 10.11 *Roots absorb air from the soil*

Can you guess what would happen if a potted plant is overwatered?

In this chapter you learnt that respiration is a vital biological process. All living organisms need to respire to get the energy needed for their survival.

Keywords

Aerobic respiration	Diaphragm	Inhalation
Anaerobic respiration	Exhalation	Spiracles
Breathing rate	Gills	Tracheae
Cellular respiration	Lungs	Ribs

What you have learnt

- Respiration is essential for survival of living organisms. It releases energy from the food.

- The oxygen we inhale is used to breakdown glucose into carbon dioxide and water. Energy is released in the process.

- The breakdown of glucose occurs in the cells of an organism (cellular respiration).

- If the food is broken down with the use of oxygen, it is called aerobic respiration. If the breakdown occurs without the use of oxygen, the respiration is called anaerobic respiration.

- During heavy exercise when the supply of oxygen to our muscle cells is insufficient, food breakdown is by anaerobic respiration.

- Breathing is a part of the process of respiration during which an organism takes in the oxygen-rich air and gives out air rich in carbon dioxide. The respiratory organs for the exchange of gases vary in different organisms.

- During inhalation, our lungs expand and then come back to the original state as the air moves out during exhalation.

- Increased physical activity enhances the rate of breathing.

- In animals like cow, buffalo, dog and cat the respiratory organs and the process of breathing are similar to those in humans.

- In earthworm, the exchange of gases occurs through the moist skin. In fishes it takes place through gills and in insects through the tracheae.

- In a plant the roots take in air present in the soil. Leaves have tiny pores called stomata through which they exchange gases. The breakdown of glucose in the plant cells is similar to that in other living beings.

Exercises

1. Why does an athlete breathe faster and deeper than usual after finishing the race?

2. List the similarities and differences between aerobic and anaerobic respiration.

3. Why do we often sneeze when we inhale a lot of dust-laden air?

4. Take three test-tubes. Fill ¾th of each with water. Label them A, B and C. Keep a snail in test-tube A, a water plant in test-tube B and in C, keep snail and plant both. Which test-tube would have the highest concentration of CO_2?

5. Tick the correct answer:

   (a) In cockroaches, air enters the body through

       (i) lungs   (ii) gills

       (iii) spiracles   (iv) skin

   (b) During heavy exercise, we get cramps in the legs due to the accumulation of

       (i) carbon dioxide   (ii) lactic acid

       (iii) alcohol   (iv) water

   (c) Normal range of breathing rate per minute in an average adult person at rest is:

       (i) 9–12   (ii) 15–18

       (iii) 21–24   (iv) 30–33

   (d) During exhalation, the ribs

       (i) move outwards   (ii) move downwards

       (iii) move upwards   (iv) do not move at all

6. Match the items in Column I with those in Column II:

Column I	Column II
(a) Yeast	(i) Earthworm
(b) Diaphragm	(ii) Gills
(c) Skin	(iii) Alcohol
(d) Leaves	(iv) Chest cavity
(e) Fish	(v) Stomata
(f) Frog	(vi) Lungs and skin
	(vii) Tracheae

7. Mark 'T' if the statement is true and 'F' if it is false:

   (i) During heavy exercise the breathing rate of a person slows down. (T/F)

   (ii) Plants carry out photosynthesis only during the day and respiration only at night. (T/F)

   (iii) Frogs breathe through their skins as well as their lungs. (T/F)

   (iv) The fishes have lungs for respiration. (T/F)

   (v) The size of the chest cavity increases during inhalation. (T/F)

8. Given below is a square of letters in which are hidden different words related to respiration in organisms. These words may be present in any direction — upwards, downwards, or along the diagonals. Find the words for your respiratory system. Clues about those words are given below the square.

S	V	M	P	L	U	N	G	S
C	Z	G	Q	W	X	N	T	L
R	M	A	T	I	D	O	T	C
I	Y	R	X	Y	M	S	R	A
B	R	H	I	A	N	T	A	Y
S	T	P	T	B	Z	R	C	E
M	I	A	M	T	S	I	H	A
S	P	I	R	A	C	L	E	S
N	E	D	K	J	N	S	A	T

   (i) The air tubes of insects

   (ii) Skeletal structures surrounding chest cavity

   (iii) Muscular floor of chest cavity

   (iv) Tiny pores on the surface of leaf

   (v) Small openings on the sides of the body of an insect

   (vi) The respiratory organs of human beings

   (vii) The openings through which we inhale

   (viii) An anaerobic organism

   (ix) An organism with tracheal system

9. The mountaineers carry oxygen with them because:

   (a) At an altitude of more than 5 km there is no air.

(b) The amount of air available to a person is less than that available on the ground.

(c) The temperature of air is higher than that on the ground.

(d) The pressure of air is higher than that on the ground.

Extended Learning — Activities and Projects

1. Observe fish in an aquarium. You will find flap like structures on both sides of their heads. These are flaps which cover the gills. These flaps open and close alternately. On the basis of these observations, explain the process of respiration in the fish.

2. Visit a local doctor. Learn about the harmful effects of smoking. You can also collect material on this topic from other sources. You can seek help of your teacher or parents. Find out the percentage of people of your area who smoke. If you have a smoker in your family, confront him with the material that you have collected.

3. Visit a doctor. Find out about artificial respiration. Ask the doctor:

   (a) When does a person need artificial respiration?

   (b) Does the person need to be kept on artificial respiration tempo rarily or permanently?

   (c) From where can the person get supply of oxygen for artificial res piration?

4. Measure the breathing rate of the members of your family and some of your friends. Investigate:

   (c) If the breathing rate of children is different from that of adults.

   (d) If the breathing rate of males is different from that of females.

   If there is a difference in any of these cases, try to find the reason.

You can read more on the following website:

www.health.howstuffworks.com/adam-200142.htm

Did you know?

For us oxygen is essential, but for those organisms which do not use it, oxygen is toxic. In fact, for humans and other organisms it may be dangerous to breathe pure oxygen for long.

11 Transportation in Animals and Plants

You have learnt earlier that all organisms need food, water and oxygen for survival. They need to transport all these to various parts of their body. Further, animals need to transport wastes to parts from where they can be removed. Have you wondered how all this is achieved? Look at Fig. 11.1. Do you see the heart and the blood vessels? They function to transport substances and together form the circulatory system. In this chapter you shall learn about transport of substances in plants and animals.

11.1 Circulatory System

Blood

What happens when you get a cut on your body? Blood flows out. But what is blood? Blood is the fluid which flows in blood vessels. It transports substances like digested food from the small intestine to the other parts of the body. It carries oxygen from the lungs to the cells of the body. It also transports waste for removal from the body.

How does the blood carry various substances? Blood is a liquid, which has cells of various kinds suspended in it.

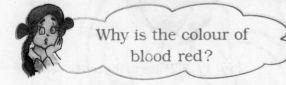

Why is the colour of blood red?

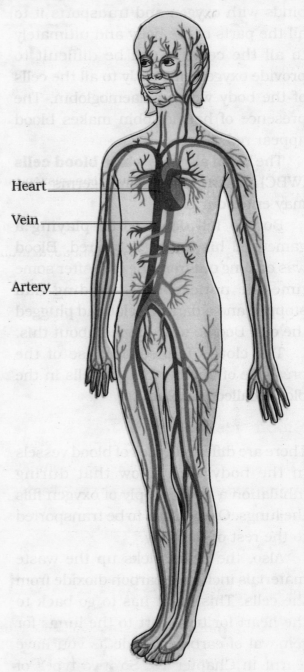

Fig. 11.1 Circulatory system
(Arteries are shown in red colour and vein in blue)

Heart

Vein

Artery

The fluid part of the blood is called **plasma**.

One type of cells are the **red blood cells** (RBC) which contain a red pigment called **haemoglobin**. Haemoglobin binds with oxygen and transports it to all the parts of the body and ultimately to all the cells. It will be difficult to provide oxygen efficiently to all the cells of the body without haemoglobin. The presence of haemoglobin makes blood appear red.

The blood also has **white blood cells** (WBC) which fight against germs that may enter our body.

Boojho fell down while playing a game and his knee got injured. Blood was coming out from the cut. After some time, he noticed that bleeding had stopped and a dark red clot had plugged the cut. Boojho was puzzled about this.

The clot is formed because of the presence of another type of cells in the blood, called **platelets**.

Blood vessels

There are different types of blood vessels in the body. You know that during inhalation a fresh supply of oxygen fills the lungs. Oxygen has to be transported to the rest of the body.

Also, the blood picks up the waste materials including carbon dioxide from the cells. This blood has to go back to the heart for transport to the lungs for removal of carbon dioxide as you have learnt in Chapter 10. So, two types of blood vessels, **arteries** and **veins** are present in the body. (Fig. 11.1)

Arteries carry oxygen-rich blood from the heart to all parts of the body. Since the blood flow is rapid and at a high pressure, the arteries have thick elastic walls.

Let us perform an activity to study the flow of blood through arteries.

Activity 11.1

Place the middle and index finger of your right hand on the inner side of your left wrist (Fig. 11.2). Can you feel some throbbing movements? Why do you think there is throbbing? This throbbing is called the **pulse** and it is due to the blood flowing in the arteries. Count the number of pulse beats in one minute.

How many pulse beats could you count? The number of beats per minute is called the **pulse rate**. A resting person, usually has a pulse rate between 72 and 80 beats per minute. Find other places in your body where you can feel the pulse.

Record your own pulse beats per minute and those of your classmates.

Fig. 11.2 *Pulse in the wrist*

Compare the values you obtained and insert them in Table 11.1.

Table 11.1 Pulse rate

S. No.	Name	Pulse per minute
1.		
2.		
3.		
4.		
5.		

Veins are the vessels which carry carbon dioxide-rich blood from all parts of the body back to the heart. The veins have thin walls. There are valves present in veins which allow blood to flow only towards the heart.

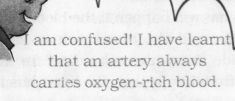

I am confused! I have learnt that an artery always carries oxygen-rich blood.

Paheli explained that the pulmonary artery carries blood from the heart, so it is called an artery and not a vein. It carries carbon dioxide-rich blood to the lungs. Pulmonary vein carries oxygen-rich blood from the lungs to the heart.

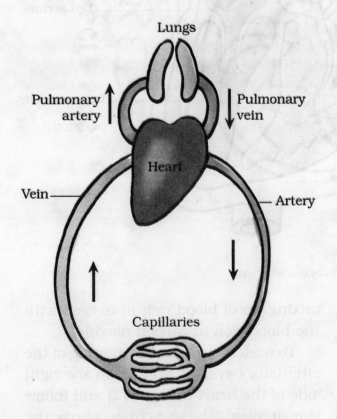

Fig. 11.3 *Schematic diagram of circulation*

Refer to Fig. 11.3. Do you see the arteries divide into smaller vessels. On reaching the tissues, they divide further into extremely thin tubes called **capillaries**. The capillaries join up to form veins which empty into the heart.

Heart

The heart is an organ which beats continuously to act as a pump for the transport of blood, which carries other substances with it.

Imagine a pump working for years without stopping! Absolutely impossible. Yet our heart works like a pump non-stop. Let us now learn about the heart.

The heart is located in the chest cavity with its lower tip slightly tilted towards the left (Fig. 11.1). Hold your fingers inwards on your palm. That makes your fist. Your heart is roughly the size of your fist.

What will happen if the blood rich in oxygen and the blood rich in carbon dioxide mix with each other? To avoid this from happening, the heart has four chambers. The two upper chambers are called the **atria** (singular: atrium) and the two lower chambers are called the **ventricles** (Fig. 11.4). The partition between the chambers helps to avoid

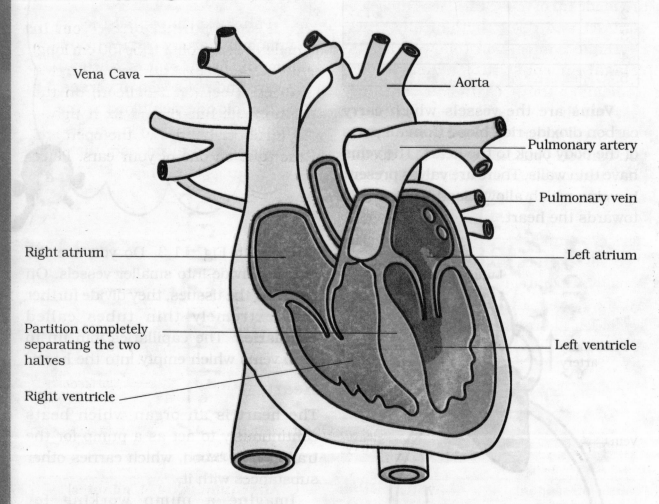

Fig. 11.4 *Sections of human heart*

Vena Cava

Aorta

Pulmonary artery

Pulmonary vein

Right atrium

Left atrium

Partition completely separating the two halves

Left ventricle

Right ventricle

Paheli wonders which side of the heart will have oxygen-rich blood and which side will have carbon dioxide-rich blood.

mixing up of blood rich in oxygen with the blood rich in carbon dioxide.

To understand the functioning of the circulatory system, start from the right side of the heart in Fig. 11.3 and follow the arrows. These arrows show the direction of the blood flow from the heart to the lungs and back to the heart from where it is pumped to the rest of the body.

Heartbeat

The walls of the chambers of the heart are made up of muscles. These muscles contract and relax rhythmically. This rhythmic contraction followed by its relaxation constitute a heartbeat. Remember that heartbeats continue every moment of our life. If you place your hand on the left side of your chest, you can feel your heartbeat. The doctor feels your heartbeats with the help of an instrument called a stethoscope.

A doctor uses the stethoscope as a device to amplify the sound of the heart. It consists of a chest piece that carries a sensitive diaphragm, two ear pieces and a tube joining the parts. Doctors can get clues about the condition of your heart by listening through a stethoscope.

Let us construct a model of a stethoscope with the materials that are available around us.

Activity 11.2

Take a small funnel of 6–7 cm in diameter. Fix a rubber tube (50 cm long) tightly on the stem of the funnel. Stretch a rubber sheet (or a balloon) on the mouth of the funnel and fix it tightly with a rubber band. Put the open end of the tube on one of your ears. Place

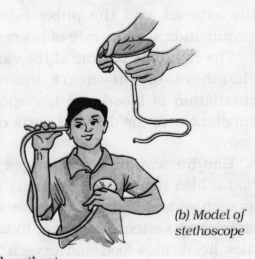
(b) Model of stethoscope

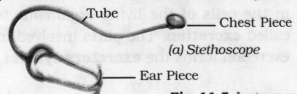
Tube

Chest Piece

(a) Stethoscope

Ear Piece

Fig. 11.5 Instrument to hear heartbeat

Table 11.2 Heartbeat and pulse rate

Name of student	While resting		After running (4–5 minutes)	
	Heartbeat	Pulse rate	Heartbeat	Pulse rate

the mouth of the funnel on your chest near the heart. Now try to listen carefully. Do you hear a regular thumping sound ? The sound is that of heart beats. How many times did your heart beat in a minute ? Count again after running for 4–5 minutes. Compare your observations.

Record your own pulse rate and heart beat and that of your friends while resting and after running and record in Table 11.2. Do you find any relationship between your heart beat and pulse rate? Each heart beat generates one pulse in the arteries and the pulse rate per minute indicates the rate of heart beat.

The rhythmic beating of the various chambers of the heart maintain circulation of blood and transport of substances to the different parts of the body.

Boojho wonders if sponges and *hydra* also have blood? Animals such as sponges and *Hydra* do not posses any circulatory system. The water in which they live brings food and oxygen as it

enters their bodies. The water carries away waste materials and carbon dioxide as it moves out. Thus, these animals do not need a circulatory fluid like the blood.

Let us now learn about the removal of waste other than carbon dioxide.

11.2 Excretion in Animals

Recall how carbon dioxide is removed as waste from the body through the lungs during exhalation. Also recall that the undigested food is removed during egestion. Let us now find out how the other waste materials are removed from the body. You may wonder where these unwanted materials come from!

When our cells perform their functions, certain waste products are released. These are toxic and hence need to be removed from the body. The process of removal of wastes produced in the cells of the living organisms is called **excretion**. The parts involved in excretion forms the **excretory system**.

Excretory system in humans

The waste which is present in the blood has to be removed from the body. How can this be done? A mechanism to filter the blood is required. This is done by the blood capillaries in the **kidneys**. When the blood reaches the two kidneys, it contains both useful and harmful substances. The useful substances are absorbed back into the blood. The wastes dissolved in water are removed as **urine**. From the kidneys, the urine goes into the urinary **bladder** through

The English physician, William Harvey (A.D. 1578–1657), discovered the circulation of blood. The current opinion in those days was that blood oscillates in the vessels of the body. For his views, Harvey was ridiculed and was called "circulator". He lost most of his patients. However, before he died, Harvey's idea about circulation was generally accepted as a biological fact.

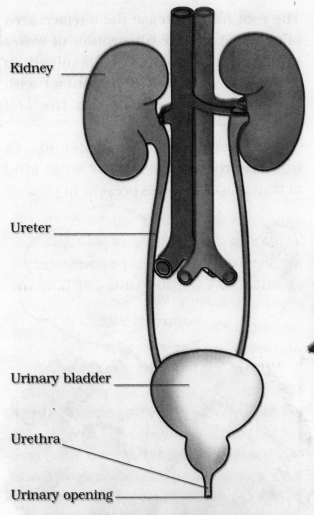

Kidney

Ureter

Urinary bladder

Urethra

Urinary opening

Fig. 11.6 *Human excretory system*

tube-like **ureters**. It is stored in the bladder and is passed out through the urinary opening at the end of a muscular tube called **urethra** (Fig. 11.6). The kindeys, ureters, bladder and urethra form the excretory system.

An adult human being normally passes about 1–1.8 L of urine in 24 hours. The urine consists of 95% water, 2.5% urea and 2.5% other waste products.

We have all experienced that we sweat on a hot summer day. The sweat contains water and salts. Boojho has seen that sometimes in summer, white patches are formed on our clothes, especially in areas like underarms. These marks are left by salts present in the sweat.

Does sweat serve any other function? We know that the water kept in an earthen pot (*matka*) is cooler. This is because the water evaporates from the pores of the pot, which causes cooling.

Paheli wants to know whether other animals also urinate?

The way in which waste chemicals are removed from the body of the animal depends on the availability of water. Aquatic animals like fishes, excrete cell waste as ammonia which directly dissolves in water. Some land animals like birds, lizards, snakes excrete a semi-solid, white coloured compound (uric acid). The major excretory product in humans is urea.

Sometimes a person's kidneys may stop working due to infection or injury. As a result of kidney failure, waste products start accumulating in the blood. Such persons cannot survive unless their blood is filtered periodically through an artificial kidney. This process is called **dialysis**.

Similarly, when we sweat, it helps to cool our body.

11.3 TRANSPORT OF SUBSTANCES IN PLANTS

In Chapter 1 you learnt that plants take water and mineral nutrients from the soil through the roots and transport it to the leaves. The leaves prepare food for the plant, using water and carbon dioxide during photosynthesis. You also learnt in Chapter 10 that food is the source of energy and every cell of an organism gets energy by the breakdown of glucose. The cells use this energy to carry out vital activities of life. Therefore food must be made available to every cell of an organism. Have you ever wondered how water and nutrients absorbed by the root are transported to the leaves? How is the food prepared by the leaves carried to the parts which cannot make food?

Transport of water and minerals

Plants absorb water and minerals by the roots. The roots have root hair.

The root hair increase the surface area of the root for the absorption of water and mineral nutrients dissolved in water. The root hair is in contact with the water present between the soil particles [Fig. 11.7 (a)].

Can you guess how water moves from the root to the leaves? What kind of transport system is present in plants?

Boojho thinks that plants may have pipes to transport water to the entire plant like we have in our homes for the supply of water.

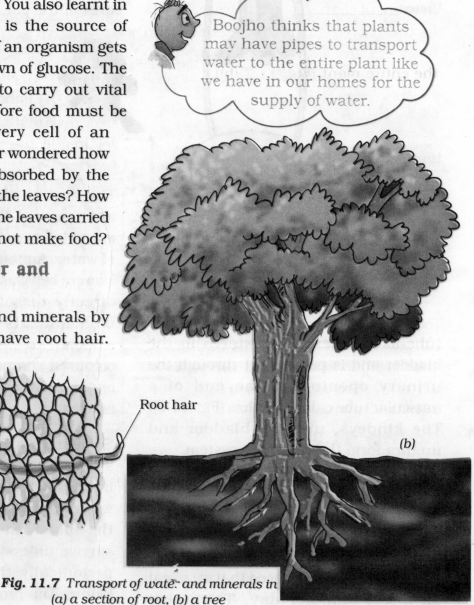

Root hair

Xylem vessels

(a)

(b)

Fig. 11.7 *Transport of water and minerals in (a) a section of root, (b) a tree*

Well, Boojho is right. Plants have pipe-like vessels to transport water and nutrients from the soil. The vessels are made of special cells, forming the **vascular tissue**. A **tissue** is a group of cells that perform specialised function in an organism. The vascular tissue for the transport of water and nutrients in the plant is called the **xylem** [Fig. 11.7 (a)].

The xylem forms a continuous network of channels that connects roots to the leaves through the stem and branches and thus transports water to the entire plant [Fig. 11.7 (b)].

Paheli says her mother puts ladyfinger and other vegetables in water if they are somewhat dry. She wants to know how water enters into them.

You know that leaves synthesise food. The food has to be transported to all parts of the plant. This is done by the vascular tissue called the **phloem**. Thus, xylem and phloem transport substances in plants.

Activity 11.3

Take a large potato and peel off its outer skin. Cut one of its ends to make the base flat. Now make a deep and hollow cavity on the opposite side. Fill half of the cavity with sugar solution and mark the level by inserting a pin in the wall of the potato (Fig. 11.8). Put the potato

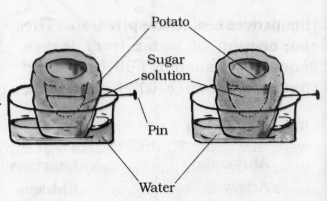

Fig. 11.8 *Transportation of water through cells*

into a dish containing a small amount of water. Make sure that the level of water is below the level of the pin. Allow the apparatus to stand for a few hours.

You would find an increase in the level of sugar solution. How did water get inside the potato? For very short distances water can move from one cell to another. In the same way water reaches xylem vessels of the root from the soil [Fig. 11.7 (a)].

Transpiration

In Class VI you learnt that plants release a lot of water by the process of transpiration.

Plants absorb mineral nutrients and water from the soil. Not all the water absorbed is utilised by the plant. The water evaporates through the stomata present on the surface of the leaves by

Boojho wants to know why plants absorb a large quantity of water from the soil, then give it off by transpiration!

the process of transpiration. The evaporation of water from leaves generates a suction pull (the same that you produce when you suck water through a straw) which can pull water to great heights in the tall trees. Transpiration also cools the plant.

Keywords

Ammonia	Heart beat	Tissue
Artery	Kidneys	Urea
Blood	Phloem	Ureter
Blood vessels	Plasma	Urethra
Capillary	Platelets	Uric acid
Circulatory system	Pulse	Urinary bladder
Dialysis	Red blood cell	Vein
Excretion	Root hair	White blood cell
Excretory system	Stethoscope	Xylem
Haemoglobin	Sweat	

What you have learnt

- In most animals the blood that circulates in the body distributes food and oxygen to different cells of the body. It also carries waste products to different parts of the body for excretion.

- Circulatory system consists of the heart and blood vessels.

- In humans, blood flows through arteries and veins and the heart acts as a pumping organ.

- Blood consists of plasma, RBC, WBC and platelets. Blood is red due to the presence of a red pigment, haemoglobin.

- The human heart beats about 70–80 times per minute in an adult person. This is called heart rate.

- Arteries carry blood from the heart to all parts of the body.

- Veins carry blood from all parts of the body back to the heart.

- Removal of waste products from the body is called excretion.

- Excretory system of humans consists of two kidneys, two ureters, a urinary bladder, and urethra.

- Salts and urea are removed along with water as sweat.

- Fish excrete waste substances such as ammonia which directly dissolve in water.
- Birds, insects and lizard excrete uric acid in semi-solid form.
- Water and mineral nutrients are absorbed by roots from the soil.
- Nutrients are transported along with water to the entire plant via the vascular tissue called xylem.
- The vascular tissue for the transport of food to the various parts of the plant is phloem.
- A lot of water is lost by plants in the form of vapour through stomata during transpiration.
- Transpiration generates a force which pulls up water absorbed by the roots from the soil, to reach the stem and leaves.

Exercises

1. Match structures given in Column I with functions given in Column II.

Column I	Column II
(i) Stomata	(a) Absorption of water
(ii) Xylem	(b) Transpiration
(iii) Root hairs	(c) Transport of food
(iv) Phloem	(d) Transport of water
	(e) Synthesis of carbohydrates

2. Fill in the blanks.

   (i) The blood from the heart is transported to all parts of the body by the _____ .

   (ii) Haemoglobin is present in _____ cells.

   (iii) Arteries and veins are joined by a network of _____ .

   (iv) The rhythmic expansion and contraction of the heart is called _____ .

   (v) The main excretory product in human beings is _____ .

   (vi) Sweat contains water and _____ .

   (vii) Kidneys eliminate the waste materials in the liquid form called _____ .

   (viii) Water reaches great heights in the trees because of suction pull caused by _____ .

3. Choose the correct option:

    (a) In plants, water is transported through

        (i) xylem   (ii) phloem

        (iii) stomata   (iv) root hair

    (b) Water absorption through roots can be increased by keeping the plants

        (i) in the shade

        (ii) in dim light

        (iii) under the fan

        (iv) covered with a polythene bag

4. Why is transport of materials necessary in a plant or in an animal? Explain.

5. What will happen if there are no platelets in the blood?

6. What are stomata? Give two functions of stomata.

7. Does transpiration serve any useful function in the plants? Explain.

8. What are the components of blood?

9. Why is blood needed by all the parts of a body?

10. What makes the blood look red?

11. Describe the function of the heart.

12. Why is it necessary to excrete waste products?

13. Draw a diagram of the human excretory system and label the various parts.

Extended Learning — Activities and Projects

1. Find out about blood groups and their importance.

2. When a person suffers from chest pain, the doctor immediately takes an ECG. Visit a doctor and get information about ECG. You may even look up an encyclopaedia or the internet.

You can read more on the following website:

www.health.howstuffworks.com/adam-200142.htm

Did you know?

There is no substitute for blood. If people lose blood from surgery or injury or if their bodies cannot produce enough blood, there is only one way to get it — through transfusion of blood donated by volunteers. Blood is usually in short supply. Donating blood does not decrease the strength of the donors.

12 Reproduction in Plants

To produce its kind is a characteristic of all living organisms. You have already learnt this in Class VI. The production of new individuals from their parents is known as **reproduction**. But, how do plants reproduce? There are different modes of reproduction in plants which we shall learn in this chapter.

12.1 Modes of Reproduction

In Class VI you learnt about different parts of a flowering plant. Try to list the various parts of a plant and write the functions of each. Most plants have roots, stems and leaves. These are called the **vegetative parts** of a plant. After a certain period of growth, most plants bear flowers. You may have seen the mango trees flowering in spring. It is these flowers that give rise to juicy mango fruit we enjoy in summer. We eat the fruits and usually discard the seeds. Seeds germinate and form new plants. So, what is the function of flowers in plants? The flowers perform the function of reproduction in plants. Flowers are the **reproductive parts** of a plant. A flower may have either the male part or the female part or both male and female parts.

There are several ways by which plants produce their offspring. These are categorised into two types: (i) asexual, and (ii) sexual reproduction. In **asexual reproduction** plants can give rise to new plants without seeds, whereas in **sexual reproduction**, new plants are obtained from seeds.

Paheli thought that new plants always grow from seeds. But, she has never seen the seeds of sugarcane, potato and rose. She wants to know how these plants reproduce.

Asexual reproduction

In asexual reproduction new plants are obtained without production of seeds or spores.

Vegetative propagation

It is a type of asexual reproduction in which new plants are produced from roots, stems, leaves and buds. Since reproduction is through the vegetative parts of the plant, it is known as **vegetative propagation.**

Activity 12.1

Cut a branch of rose or *champa* with a node. This piece of branch is termed a **cutting**. Bury the cutting in the soil. A node is a part of the stem/branch at which a leaf arises (Fig. 12.1). Water the cutting every day and observe its growth. Observe and record the number of days taken for roots to come out and new leaves to arise. Try the same activity by growing money plant in a jar of water and record your observations.

Fig. 12.1 *Stem-cutting of rose*

Node

Bud in the axil

You must have seen flower buds developing into flowers. Apart from flower buds, there are buds in the axil (point of attachment of the leaf at the node) of leaves which develop into shoots. These buds are called vegetative buds (Fig. 12.2). A bud consists of a short stem around which immature overlapping leaves are folded. The vegetative buds can also give rise to new plants.

Activity 12.2

Take a fresh potato. Observe the scars on it with the help of a magnifying glass. You may find bud(s) in them. These scars are also called **"eyes"**. Cut a few pieces

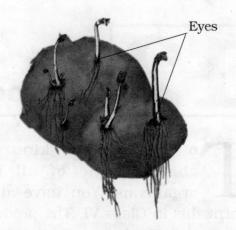

Eyes

Fig. 12.2 *Potato plant sprouting from an 'eye'*

of a potato, each with an eye and bury them in the soil. Water the pieces regularly for a few days and observe their progress. What do you find?

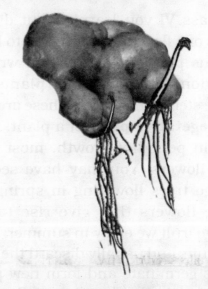

Fig. 12.3 *Ginger with new plants sprouting from it*

Likewise you can also grow ginger (Fig. 12.3) or turmeric.

Bryophyllum (sprout leaf plant) has buds in the margins of leaves (Fig. 12.4). If a leaf of this plant falls on a moist soil, each bud can give rise to a new plant.

Fig. 12.4 *Leaf of Bryophyllum with buds in the margin*

The roots of some plants can also give rise to new plants. Sweet potato and dahlia are examples.

Plants such as cacti produce new plants when their parts get detached from the main plant body. Each detached part can grow into a new plant.

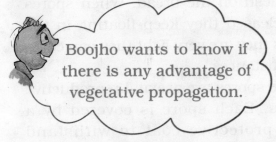

Boojho wants to know if there is any advantage of vegetative propagation.

Plants produced by vegetative propagation take less time to grow and bear flowers and fruits earlier than those produced from seeds. The new plants are exact copies of the parent plant, as they are produced from a single parent.

Later in this chapter you will learn that plants produced by sexual reproduction have characters of both the parents. Plants produce seeds as a result of sexual reproduction.

Budding

You have already learnt about the tiny organisms like yeast can be seen only under a microscope. These grow and

multiply every few hours if sufficient nutrients are made available to them. Remember that yeast is a single-celled organism. Let us see how they reproduce?

Activity 12.3

(To be demonstrated by the teacher)
Take a piece of yeast cake or yeast powder from a bakery or a chemist shop. Take a pinch of yeast and place it in a container with some water. Add a spoonful of sugar and shake to dissolve it. Keep it in the warm part of a room. After an hour, put a drop of this liquid on a glass slide and observe under a microscope. What do you observe? You may see the formation of new yeast cells (Fig. 12.5).

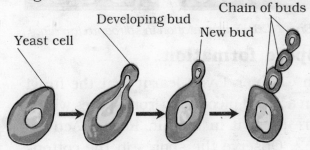

Fig. 12.5 *Reproduction in yeast by budding*

The small bulb-like projection coming out from the yeast cell is called a **bud**. The bud gradually grows and gets detached from the parent cell and forms a new yeast cell. The new yeast cell grows, matures and produces more yeast cells. Sometimes, another bud arises from the bud forming a chain of buds. If this process continues, a large number of yeast cells are produced in a short time.

Fragmentation

You might have seen slimy green patches in ponds, or in other stagnant water bodies. These are the algae. When water and nutrients are available algae grow and multiply rapidly by fragmentation. An alga breaks up into two or more fragments. These fragments or pieces grow into new individuals (Fig. 12.6). This process continues and they cover a large area in a short period of time.

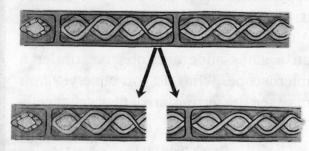

Fig. 12.6 *Fragmentation in spirogyra (an alga)*

Spore formation

In Chapter 1 you learnt that the fungi on a bread piece grow from spores which are present in the air. Repeat Activity 1.2. Observe the spores in the cotton-

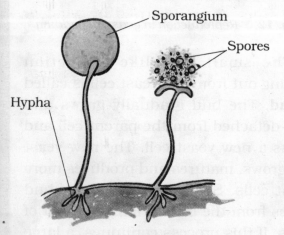

Fig. 12.7 *Reproduction through spore formation in fungus*

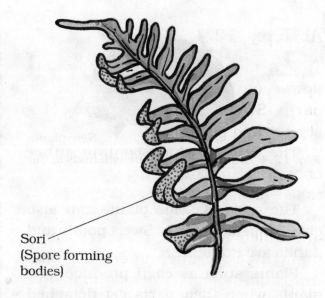

Sori
(Spore forming bodies)

Fig. 12.8 *Reproduction through spore formation in fern*

like mesh on the bread. When spores are released they keep floating in the air. As they are very light they can cover long distances.

The spores are asexual reproductive bodies. Each spore is covered by a hard protective coat to withstand unfavourable conditions such as high temperature and low humidity. So they can survive for a long time. Under favourable conditions, a spore germinates and develops into a new individual. Plants such as moss and ferns (Fig. 12.8) also reproduce by means of spores.

12.2 Sexual Reproduction

You have learnt earlier the structure of a flower. You know that the flowers are the reproductive parts of a plant. The **stamens** are the male reproductive part and the **pistil** is the female reproductive part (Fig. 12.9).

Activity 12.4

Take a mustard/china rose/petunia flower and separate its reproductive parts. Study the various parts of a stamen and pistil.

The flowers which contain either only the pistil or only the stamens are called **unisexual flowers**. The flowers which contain both stamens and pistil are called **bisexual flowers**. Corn, papaya and cucumber produce unisexual flowers, whereas mustard, rose and petunia have bisexual flowers.

Both the male and the female unisexual flowers may be present in the same plant or in different plants.

Could you identify the anther and the filament of a stamen? [Fig. 12.9 (a)]. Anther contains pollen grains which produce **male gametes**. A pistil consists of stigma, style and ovary. The ovary contains one or more ovules. The **female gamete** or the **egg** is formed in an ovule [Fig. 12.9 (b)]. In sexual reproduction a male and a female gamete fuse to form a **zygote**.

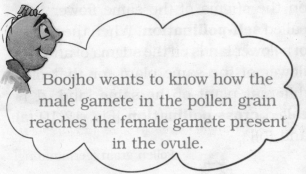

Boojho wants to know how the male gamete in the pollen grain reaches the female gamete present in the ovule.

Pollination

Generally pollen grains have a tough protective coat which prevents them from drying up. Since pollen grains are light, they can be carried by wind or

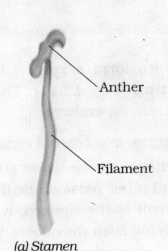

Anther

Filament

(a) Stamen

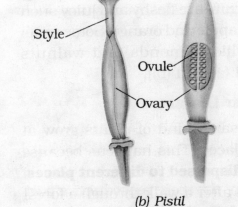

Stigma

Style

Ovule

Ovary

(b) Pistil

Fig. 12.9 *Reproductive parts*

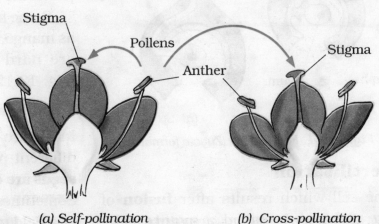

Stigma

Pollens

Anther

Stigma

(a) Self-pollination

(b) Cross-pollination

Fig. 12.10 *Pollination in flower*

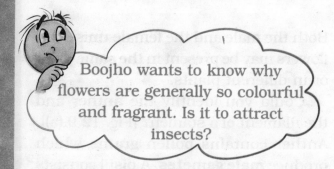

Boojho wants to know why flowers are generally so colourful and fragrant. Is it to attract insects?

water. Insects visit flowers and carry away pollen on their bodies. Some of the pollen lands on the stigma of a flower of the same kind. The transfer of pollen from the anther to the stigma of a flower is called **pollination**. If the pollen lands on the stigma of the same flower it is called **self-pollination**. When the pollen of a flower lands on the stigma of another flower of the same plant, or that of a different plant of the same kind, it is called **cross-pollination** [Fig. 12.10 (a) and (b)].

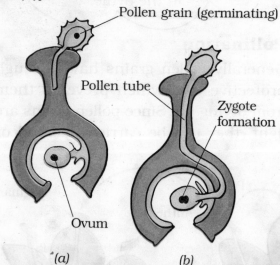

Fig. 12.11 Fertilisation (Zygote formation)

Fertilisation

The cell which results after **fusion** of the gametes is called a **zygote**. The process of fusion of male and female

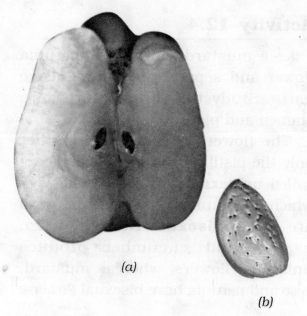

Fig. 12.12 (a) Section of an apple, (b) Almond

gametes (to form a zygote) is called **fertilisation** (Fig. 12.11). The zygote develops into an **embryo**.

12.3 Fruits and Seed Formation

After fertilisation, the ovary grows into a fruit and other parts of the flower fall off. The fruit is the ripened ovary. The seeds develop from the ovules. The seed contains an embryo enclosed in a protective seed coat.

Some fruits are fleshy and juicy such as mango, apple and orange. Some fruits are hard like almonds and walnuts [Fig. 12.12 (a) and (b)].

12.4 Seed Dispersal

In nature same kind of plants grow at different places. This happens because **seeds are dispersed to different places**. Sometimes after a walk through a forest or a field or a park, you may have found seeds or fruits sticking to your clothes.

Did you try to observe how these seeds were clinging to your clothes?

What do you think will happen if all seeds of a plant were to fall at the same place and grow there? There would be severe competition for sunlight, water, minerals and space. As a result the seeds would not grow into healthy plants. Plants benefit by seed dispersal. It prevents competition between the plant and its own seedlings for sunlight, water and minerals. It also enables the plants to invade new habitats for wider distribution.

Seeds and fruits of plants are carried away by wind, water and animals. Winged seeds such as those of drumstick and maple [Fig. 12.13 (a) and (b)], light seeds of grasses or hairy seeds of aak (*Madar*) and hairy fruit of sunflower [Fig. 12.14 (a), (b)], get blown off with the wind to far away places. Some seeds are dispersed by water. These fruits or seeds usually develop floating ability in the form of spongy or fibrous outer coat as in coconut. Some seeds are dispersed by animals, especially spiny seeds with hooks which get attached to the bodies of animals and are carried to distant places. Examples are *Xanthium* (Fig. 12.15) and *Urena*.

Some seeds are dispersed when the fruits burst with sudden jerks. The seeds are scattered far from the parent plant. This happens in the case of castor and balsam.

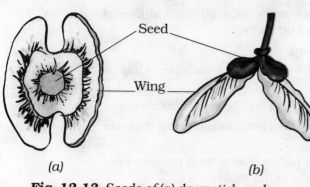

(a)   (b)

Fig. 12.13 *Seeds of (a) drumstick and (b) maple*

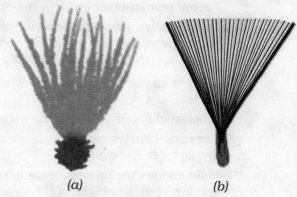

(a)   (b)

Fig. 12.14 *(a) The hairy fruit of sunflower and (b) hairy seed of madar (aak)*

Fig. 12.15 *Xanthium*

Keywords

Asexual reproduction	Hypha	Sexual reproduction
Budding	Ovule	Spore
Embryo	Pollen grain	Sporangium
Fertilisation	Pollen tube	Vegetative propagation
Fragmentation	Pollination	Zygote
Gametes	Seed dispersal	

What you have learnt

- All organisms multiply or reproduce their own kind.
- In plants there are two modes of reproduction, asexual and sexual.
- There are several methods of asexual reproduction such as fragmentation, budding, spore formation and vegetative propagation.
- Sexual reproduction involves the fusion of male and female gametes.
- In vegetative propagation new plants are produced from different vegetative parts such as leaves, stems and roots.
- Flower is the reproductive part of a plant.
- A flower may be unisexual with either the male or the female reproductive parts.
- A bisexual flower has both the male and the female reproductive parts.
- The male gametes are found inside the pollen grains and female gametes are found in the ovule.
- Pollination is the process of transfer of pollen grains from the anther of one flower to the stigma of the same or another flower.
- Pollination is of two types, self-pollination and cross-pollination. In self-pollination, pollen grains are transferred from the anther to the stigma of the same flower. In cross-pollination, pollen grains are transferred from the anther of one flower to the stigma of another flower of the same kind.
- Pollination takes place in plants with the help of wind, water and insects.
- The fusion of male and female gametes is called fertilisation.
- Fertilised egg is called zygote. Zygote develops into an embryo.
- Fruit is the mature ovary whereas ovule develops into a seed, which contains the developing embryo.
- Seed dispersal is aided by wind, water and animals.
- Seed dispersal helps the plants to (i) prevent overcrowding, (ii) avoid competition for sunlight, water and minerals and (iii) invade new habitats.

Exercises

1. Fill in the blanks:

   (a) Production of new individuals from the vegetative part of parent is called_____.

   (b) A flower may have either male or female reproductive parts. Such a flower is called_____.

   (c) The transfer of pollen grains from the anther to the stigma of the same or of another flower of the same kind is known as _____.

   (d) The fusion of male and female gametes is termed as _____.

   (e) Seed dispersal takes place by means of _____, _____ and _____.

2. Describe the different methods of asexual reproduction. Give examples.

3. Explain what you understand by sexual reproduction.

4. State the main difference between asexual and sexual reproduction.

5. Sketch the reproductive parts of a flower.

6. Explain the difference between self-pollination and cross-pollination.

7. How does the process of fertilisation take place in flowers?

8. Describe the various ways by which seeds are dispersed.

9. Match items in Column I with those in Column II:

Column I		Column II	
(a)	Bud	(i)	Maple
(b)	Eyes	(ii)	*Spirogyra*
(c)	Fragmentation	(iii)	Yeast
(d)	Wings	(iv)	Bread mould
(e)	Spores	(v)	Potato
		(vi)	Rose

10. Tick (✓) the correct answer:

    (a) The reproductive part of a plant is the

        (i) leaf   (ii) stem   (iii) root   (iv) flower

    (b) The process of fusion of the male and the female gametes is called

        (i) fertilisation   (ii) pollination

        (iii) reproduction   (iv) seed formation

(c) Mature ovary forms the

    (i)   seed   (ii)   stamen

    (iii) pistil   (iv) fruit

(d) A spore producing plant is

    (i)   rose   (ii)   bread mould

    (iii) potato   (iv) ginger

(e) *Bryophyllum* can reproduce by its

    (i)   stem   (ii)   leaves

    (iii) roots   (iv) flower

Extended Learning—Activities and Projects

1. Make your own cactus garden by collecting pieces cut from different kinds of cacti. Grow the variety in one single flat container or in separate pots.

2. Visit a fruit market and collect as many local fruits as possible. If many fruits are not available, you can collect tomatoes and cucumbers (these are fruits, though we use them as vegetables). Make drawings of the different fruits. Split the fruits and examine the seeds within. Look for any special characteristics in the fruits and their seeds. If possible visit the website:

   www.saps.plantsci.cam.ac.uk/fscfruit/dispersal.pdf

   You can visit a library also to learn about this.

3. Think of ten different fruit-bearing plants. Remember that many vegetables are also fruits of the plants. Discuss with your teacher, parents, farmers, fruit growers and agricultural experts (if available nearby) and find out the manner of their dispersal. Present your data in the form of a table as shown below:

S. No.	Name of fruit-bearing plant	Agent through which seeds are dispersed	Part of or seed which helps in dispersal
1.			
2.			
3.			

4. Suppose there is one member of a particular kind of organism in a culture dish, which doubles itself in one hour through asexual reproduction. Work out the number of members of that kind of organism which will be present in the culture dish after ten hours. Such a colony of individuals arising from one parent is called a "clone".

You can read more on the following website:

www.edumedia-sciences.com/a437_l2-blog-call.html

13 Motion and Time

In Class VI, you learnt about different types of motions. You learnt that a motion could be along a straight line, it could be circular or periodic. Can you recall these three types of motions?

Table 13.1 gives some common examples of motions. Identify the type of motion in each case.

Table 13.1 Some examples of different types of motion

Example of motion	Type of motion Along a straight line/circular/ periodic
Soldiers in a march past	
Bullock cart moving on a straight road	
Hands of an athlete in a race	
Pedal of a bicycle in motion	
Motion of the earth around the sun	
Motion of a swing	
Motion of a pendulum	

It is common experience that the motion of some objects is slow while that of some others is fast.

13.1 Slow or Fast

We know that some vehicles move faster than others. Even the same vehicle may move faster or slower at different times. Make a list of ten objects moving along a straight path. Group the motion of these objects as slow and fast. How did you decide which object is moving slow and which one is moving fast?

If vehicles are moving on a road in the same direction, we can easily tell which one of them is moving faster than the other.

Activity 13.1

Look at Fig. 13.1. It shows the position of some vehicles moving on a road in the same direction at some instant of time. Now look at Fig. 13.2. It shows the position of the same vehicles after some time. From your observation of the two figures, answer the following questions:

Which vehicle is moving the fastest of all? Which one of them is moving the slowest of all?

The distance moved by objects in a given interval of time can help us to decide which one is faster or slower. For example, imagine that you have gone to see off your friend at the bus stand. Suppose you start pedalling your bicycle at the same time as the bus begins to move. The distance covered by you after

Fig. 13.1 *Vehicles moving in the same direction on a road*

Fig. 13.2 *Position of vehicles shown in Fig. 13.1 after some time*

5 minutes would be much smaller than that covered by the bus. Would you say that the bus is moving faster than the bicycle?

We often say that the faster vehicle has a higher speed. In a 100-metre race

it is easy to decide whose speed is the highest. One who takes shortest time to cover the distance of 100 metres has the highest speed.

13.2 Speed

You are probably familiar with the word speed. In the examples given above, a higher speed seems to indicate that a given distance has been covered in a shorter time, or a larger distance covered in a given time.

The most convenient way to find out which of the two or more objects is moving faster is to compare the distances moved by them in a unit time. Thus, if we know the distance covered by two buses in one hour, we can tell which one is slower. We call the distance covered by an object in a unit time as the **speed** of the object.

When we say that a car is moving with a speed of 50 kilometres per hour, it implies that it will cover a distance of 50 kilometres in one hour. However, a car seldom moves with a constant speed for one hour. In fact, it starts moving slowly and then picks up speed. So, when we say that the car has a speed of 50 kilometres per hour, we usually consider only the total distance covered by it in one hour. We do not bother whether the car has been moving with a constant speed or not during that hour. The speed calculated here is actually the average speed of the car. In this book **we shall use the term speed for average speed**. So, for us the **speed is the total distance covered divided by the total time taken**. Thus,

$$\text{Speed} = \frac{\text{Total distance covered}}{\text{Total time taken}}$$

> In everyday life we seldom find objects moving with a constant speed over long distances or for long durations of time. If the speed of an object moving along a straight line keeps changing, its motion is said to be **non-uniform**. On the other hand, an object moving along a straight line with a constant speed is said to be in **uniform motion**. In this case, the average speed is the same as the actual speed.

We can determine the speed of a given object once we can measure the time taken by it to cover a certain distance. In Class VI you learnt how to measure distances. But, how do we measure time? Let us find out.

13.3 MEASUREMENT OF TIME

If you did not have a clock, how would you decide what time of the day it is? Have you ever wondered how our elders could tell the approximate time of the day by just looking at shadows?

How do we measure time interval of a month? A year?

Our ancestors noticed that many events in nature repeat themselves after definite intervals of time. For example,

they found that the sun rises everyday in the morning. The time between one sunrise and the next was called a day. Similarly, a month was measured from one new moon to the next. A year was fixed as the time taken by the earth to complete one revolution of the sun.

Often we need to measure intervals of time which are much shorter than a day. Clocks or watches are perhaps the most common time measuring devices. Have you ever wondered how clocks and watches measure time?

The working of clocks is rather complex. But all of them make use of some periodic motion. One of the most well-known periodic motions is that of a **simple pendulum**.

(a) Wall clock

(b) Table clock

(c) Digital clock

Fig. 13.3 *Some common clocks*

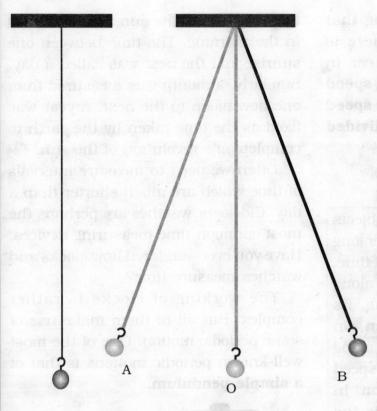

Fig. 13.4 (a) A simple pendulum

Fig. 13.4 (b) Different positions of the bob of an oscillating simple pendulum

A simple pendulum consists of a small metallic ball or a piece of stone suspended from a rigid stand by a thread [Fig. 13.4 (a)]. The metallic ball is called the **bob** of the pendulum.

Fig. 13.4 (a) shows the pendulum at rest in its mean position. When the bob of the pendulum is released after taking it slightly to one side, it begins to move to and fro [Fig. 13.4 (b)]. The to and fro motion of a simple pendulum is an example of a periodic or an **oscillatory** motion.

The pendulum is said to have completed one **oscillation** when its bob, starting from its mean position O, moves to A, to B and back to O. The pendulum also completes one oscillation when its bob moves from one extreme position A to the other extreme position B and comes back to A. The time taken by the pendulum to complete one oscillation is called its **time period**.

Activity 13.2

Set up a simple pendulum as shown in Fig. 13.4 (a) with a thread or string of length nearly one metre. Switch off any fans nearby. Let the bob of the pendulum come to rest at its mean position. Mark the mean position of the bob on the floor below it or on the wall behind it.

To measure the time period of the pendulum we will need a stopwatch. However, if a stopwatch is not available, a table clock or a wristwatch can be used.

To set the pendulum in motion, gently hold the bob and move it slightly to one side. Make sure that the string attached to the bob is taut while you displace it. Now release the bob from its displaced position. Remember that the bob is not to be pushed when it is released. Note the time on the clock when the bob is at its mean position. Instead of the mean position you may note the time when the bob is at one of its extreme positions. Measure the time the pendulum takes to complete 20 oscillations. Record your observations in Table 13.2. The first observation shown is just a sample. Your observations could be different from this. Repeat this activity a few times and record your observations. By dividing the time taken for 20 oscillations by 20, get the time taken for one oscillation, or the time period of the pendulum.

Is the time period of your pendulum nearly the same in all cases?

Note that a slight change in the initial displacement does not affect the time period of your pendulum.

Nowadays most clocks or watches have an electric circuit with one or more cells. These clocks are called quartz clocks. The time measured by quartz clocks is much more accurate than that by the clocks available earlier.

Units of time and speed

The basic unit of time is a **second**. Its symbol is s. Larger units of time are minutes (min) and hours (h). You already know how these units are related to one another.

What would be the basic unit of speed?

Since the speed is distance/time, the basic unit of speed is m/s. Of course, it could also be expressed in other units such as m/min or km/h.

You must remember that **the symbols of all units are written in singular**. For example, we write 50 km and not 50 kms, or 8 cm and not 8 cms.

Boojho is wondering how many seconds there are in a day and how many hours in a year. Can you help him?

Table 13.2 Time period of a simple pendulum

Length of the string = 100 cm

S.No.	Time taken for 20 oscillations	Time period
1.	42 s	2.1 s
2.		
3.		

There is an interesting story about the discovery that the time period of a given pendulum is constant. You might have heard the name of famous scientist Galileo Galilie (A.D. 1564 –1642). It is said that once Galileo was sitting in a church. He noticed that a lamp suspended from the ceiling with a chain was moving slowly from one side to the other. He was surprised to find that his pulse beat the same number of times during the interval in which the lamp completed one oscillation. Galileo experimented with various pendulums to verify his observation. He found that a pendulum of a given length takes always the same time to complete one oscillation. This observation led to the development of pendulum clocks. Winding clocks and wristwatches were refinements of the pendulum clocks.

Different units of time are used depending on the need. For example, it is convenient to express your age in years rather than in days or hours. Similarly, it will not be wise to express in years the time taken by you to cover the distance between your home and your school.

How small or large is a time interval of one second? The time taken in saying aloud "two thousand and one" is nearby one second. Verify it by counting aloud from "two thousand and one" to "two thousand and ten". The pulse of a normal healthy adult at rest beats about 72 times in a minute that is about 12 times in 10 seconds. This rate may be slightly higher for children.

> Paheli wondered how time was measured when pendulum clocks were not available.

Many time measuring devices were used in different parts of the world before the pendulum clocks became popular. Sundials, water clocks and sand clocks are some examples of such devices. Different designs of these devices were developed in different parts of the world (Fig. 13.5).

13.4 Measuring Speed

Having learnt how to measure time and distance, you can calculate the speed of an object. Let us find the speed of a ball moving along the ground.

Activity 13.3

Draw a straight line on the ground with chalk powder or lime and ask one of your friends to stand 1 to 2 m away from it. Let your friend gently roll a ball along the ground in a direction perpendicular to the line. Note the time at the moment the ball crosses the line and also when it comes to rest (Fig. 13.6). How much time does the ball take to come to rest?

The smallest time interval that can be measured with commonly available clocks and watches is one second. However, now special clocks are available that can measure time intervals smaller than a second. Some of these clocks can measure time intervals as small as one millionth or even one billionth of a second. You might have heard the terms like microsecond and nanosecond. One microsecond is one millionth of a second. A nanosecond is one billionth of a second. Clocks that measure such small time intervals are used for scientific research. The time measuring devices used in sports can measure time intervals that are one tenth or one hundredth of a second. On the other hand, times of historical events are stated in terms of centuries or millenniums. The ages of stars and planet are often expressed in billions of years. Can you imagine the range of time intervals that we have to deal with?

(b) Sand clock

(c) Water clock

(a) Sundial at Jantar Mantar, Delhi

Fig. 13.5 *Some ancient time-measuring devices*

Fig. 13.6 *Measuring the speed of a ball*

Measure the distance between the point at which the ball crosses the line and the point where it comes to rest. You can use a scale or a measuring tape. Let different groups repeat the activity. Record the measurements in Table 13.3. In each case calculate the speed of the ball.

You may now like to compare your speed of walking or cycling with that of your friends. You need to know the distance of the school from your home or from some other point. Each one of you can then measure the time taken to cover that distance and calculate your speed. It may be interesting to know who amongst you is the fastest. Speeds of some living organisms are given in

Table 13.3 Distance moved and time taken by a moving ball

Name of the group	Distance moved by the ball (m)	Time taken (s)	Speed = Distance/ Time taken (m/s)

Table 13.4, in km/h. You can calculate the speeds in m/s yourself.

Rockets, launching satellites into earth's orbit, often attain speeds up to 8 km/s. On the other hand, a tortoise can move only with a speed of about 8 cm/s. Can you calculate how fast is the rocket compared with the tortoise?

Once you know the speed of an object, you can find the distance moved by it in a given time. All you have to do is to multiply the speed by time. Thus,

Distance covered = Speed × Time

You can also find the time an object would take to cover a distance while moving with a given speed.

Time taken = Distance/Speed

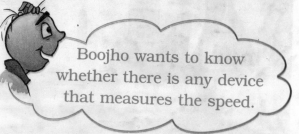

Boojho wants to know whether there is any device that measures the speed.

You might have seen a meter fitted on top of a scooter or a motorcycle. Similarly, meters can be seen on the dashboards of cars, buses and other vehicles. Fig. 13.7 shows the dashboard of a car. Note that one of the meters has km/h written at one corner. This is called a **speedometer**. It records the

Table 13.4 Fastest speed that some animals can attain

S. No.	Name of the object	Speed in km/h	Speed in m/s
1.	Falcon	320	$\dfrac{320 \times 1000}{60 \times 60}$
2.	Cheetah	112	
3.	Blue fish	40 – 46	
4.	Rabbit	56	
5.	Squirrel	19	
6.	Domestic mouse	11	
7.	Human	40	
8.	Giant tortoise	0.27	
9.	Snail	0.05	

Fig. 13.7 *The dashboard of a car*

13.5 DISTANCE-TIME GRAPH

You might have seen that newspapers, magazines, etc., present information in various forms of graphs to make it

Table 13.5 Odometer reading at different times of the journey

Time (AM)	Odometer reading	Distance from the starting point
8:00 AM	36540 km	0 km
8:30 AM	36560 km	20 km
9:00 AM	36580 km	40 km
9:30 AM	36600 km	60 km
10:00 AM	36620 km	80 km

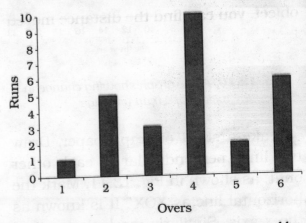

Fig. 13.8 *A bar graph showing runs scored by a team in each over*

speed directly in km/h. There is also another meter that measures the distance moved by the vehicle. This meter is known as an **odometer**.

While going for a school picnic, Paheli decided to note the reading on the odometer of the bus after every 30 minutes till the end of the journey. Later on she recorded her readings in Table 13.5.

Can you tell how far was the picnic spot from the school? Can you calculate the speed of the bus? Looking at the Table, Boojho teased Paheli whether she can tell how far they would have travelled till 9:45 AM. Paheli had no answer to this question. They went to their teacher. She told them that one way to solve this problem is to plot a distance-time graph. Let us find out how such a graph is plotted.

interesting. The type of graph shown in Fig. 13.8 is known as a bar graph. Another type of graphical representation is a pie chart (Fig. 13.9). The graph shown in Fig. 13.10 is an example of a line graph. The distance-time graph is a line graph. Let us learn to make such a graph.

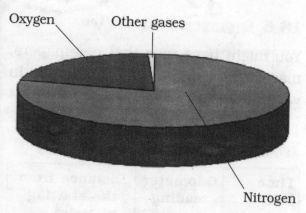

Fig. 13.9 A pie chart showing composition of air

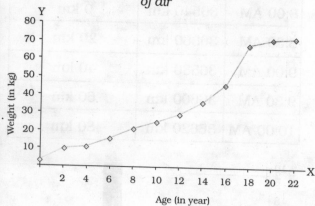

Fig. 13.10 A line graph showing change in weight of a man with age

Take a sheet of graph paper. Draw two lines perpendicular to each other on it, as shown in Fig. 13.11. Mark the horizontal line as XOX′. It is known as the x-axis. Similarly mark the vertical line YOY′. It is called the y-axis. The point of intersection of XOX′ and YOY′ is known as the origin O. The two quantities between which the graph is drawn are shown along these two axes. We show the positive values on the x-axis along OX. Similarly, positive values on the y-axis are shown along OY. In this chapter we shall consider only the positive values of quantities.

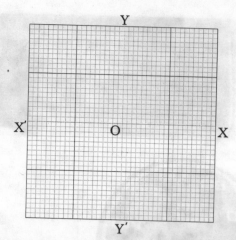

Fig. 13.11 x-axis and y-axis on a graph paper

Therefore, we shall use only the shaded part of the graph shown in Fig. 13.11.

Boojho and Paheli found out the distance travelled by a car and the time taken by it to cover that distance. Their data is shown in Table 13.6.

Table 13.6 The motion of a car

S. No.	Time	Distance
1.	0	0
2.	1 min	1 km
3.	2 min	2 km
4.	3 min	3 km
5.	4 min	4 km
6.	5 min	5 km

You can make the graph by following the steps given below:

• Draw two perpendicular lines to represent the two axes and mark them as OX and OY as in Fig. 13.11.
• Decide the quantity to be shown along the x-axis and that to be shown along the y-axis. In this case

we show the time along the x-axis and the distance along the y-axis.

- Choose a scale to represent the distance and another to represent the time on the graph. For the motion of the car scales could be

  Time: 1 min = 1 cm

  Distance: 1 km = 1 cm

- Mark values for the time and the distance on the respective axes according to the scale you have chosen. For the motion of the car mark the time 1 min, 2 min, ... on the x-axis from the origin O. Similarly, mark the distance 1 km, 2 km ... on the y-axis (Fig. 13.12).

- Now you have to mark the points on the graph paper to represent each set of values for distance and time. Observation recorded at S. No. 1 in Table 13.6 shows that at time 0 min the distance moved is also zero. The point corresponding to this set of values on the graph will therefore be the origin itself. After 1 minute, the car has moved a distance of 1 km. To mark this set of values look for the point that represents 1 minute on the x-axis. Draw a line parallel to the y-axis at this point. Then draw a line parallel to the x-axis from the point corresponding to distance 1 km on the y-axis. The point where these two lines intersect represents this set of values on the graph (Fig. 13.12). Similarly, mark on the graph paper the points corresponding to different sets of values.

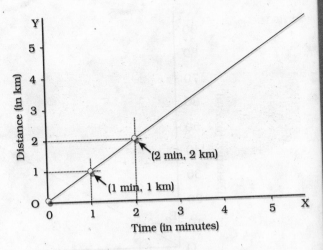

Fig. 13.12 *Making a graph*

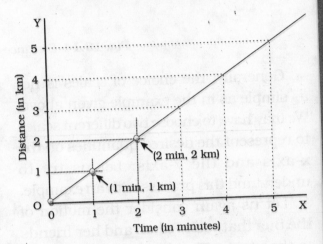

Fig. 13.13 *Making a graph*

- Fig. 13.13 shows the set of points on the graph corresponding to positions of the car at various times.

- Join all the points on the graph as shown in Fig. 13.13. It is a straight line. This is the distance-time graph for the motion of the car.

- If the distance-time graph is a straight line, it indicates that the object is moving with a constant speed. However, if the speed of the object keeps changing, the graph can be of any shape.

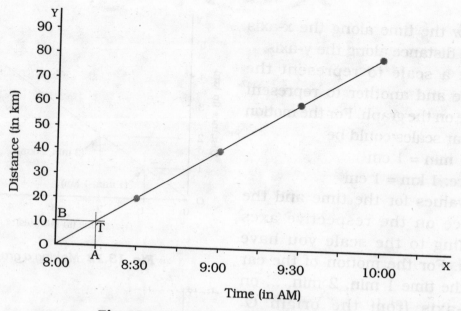

Fig. 13.14 *Distance-time graph of the bus*

Generally, the choice of scales is not as simple as in the example given above. We may have to choose two different scales to represent the desired quantities on the x-axis and the y-axis. Let us try to understand this process with an example.

Let us again consider the motion of the bus that took Paheli and her friends to the picnic. The distance covered and time taken by the bus are shown in Table 13.5. The total distance covered by the bus is 80 km. If we decide to choose a scale 1 km = 1 cm, we shall have to draw an axis of length 80 cm. This is not possible on a sheet of paper. On the other hand, a scale 10 km = 1 cm would require an axis of length only 8 cm. This scale is quite convenient. However, the graph may cover only a small part of the graph paper. Some of the points to be kept in mind while choosing the most suitable scale for drawing a graph are:

- the difference between the highest and the lowest values of each quantity.
- the intermediate values of each quantity, so that with the scale chosen it is convenient to mark the values on the graph, and
- to utilise the maximum part of the paper on which the graph is to be drawn.

Suppose that we have a graph paper of size 25 cm × 25 cm. One of the scales which meets the above conditions and can accommodate the data of Table 13.5 could be

Distance: 5 km = 1 cm, and
Time: 6 min = 1 cm

Can you now draw the distance-time graph for the motion of the bus? Is the graph drawn by you similar to that shown in Fig. 13.13?

Distance-time graphs provide a variety of information about the motion when compared to the data presented by a table. For example, Table 13.5 gives information about the distance moved by the bus only at some definite time intervals. On the other hand, from the distance-time graph we can find the distance moved by the bus at any instant of time. Suppose we want to know how much distance the bus had travelled at 8:15 AM. We mark the point corresponding to the time (8:15 AM) on the x-axis. Suppose this point is A. Next we draw a line perpendicular to the x-axis (or parallel to the y-axis) at point A. We then mark the point, T, on the graph at which this perpendicular line intersects it (Fig. 13.14). Next, we draw a line through the point T parallel to the x-axis. This intersects the y-axis at the point B. The distance corresponding to the point B on the y-axis, OB, gives us the distance in km covered by the bus at 8:15 AM. How much is this distance in km? Can you now help Paheli to find the distance moved by the bus at 9:45 AM? Can you also find the speed of the bus from its distance-time graph?

Keywords

Bar graph

Graphs

Non-uniform motion

Oscillation

Simple pendulum

Speed

Time period

Uniform motion

Unit of time

What you have Learnt

- The distance moved by an object in a unit time is called its speed.
- Speed of objects help us to decide which one is moving faster than the other.
- The speed of an object is the distance travelled divided by the time taken to cover that distance. Its basic unit is metre per second (m/s).
- Periodic events are used for the measurement of time. Periodic motion of a pendulum has been used to make clocks and watches.
- Motion of objects can be presented in pictorial form by their distance-time graphs.
- The distance-time graph for the motion of an object moving with a constant speed is a straight line.

Exercises

1. Classify the following as motion along a straight line, circular or oscillatory motion:

    (i)   Motion of your hands while running.

    (ii) Motion of a horse pulling a cart on a straight road.

    (iii) Motion of a child in a merry-go-round.

    (iv) Motion of a child on a see-saw.

    (v)   Motion of the hammer of an electric bell.

    (vi) Motion of a train on a straight bridge.

2. Which of the following are not correct?

    (i)   The basic unit of time is second.

    (ii) Every object moves with a constant speed.

    (iii) Distances between two cities are measured in kilometres.

    (iv) The time period of a given pendulum is not constant.

    (v)   The speed of a train is expressed in m/h.

3. A simple pendulum takes 32 s to complete 20 oscillations. What is the time period of the pendulum?

4. The distance between two stations is 240 km. A train takes 4 hours to cover this distance. Calculate the speed of the train.

5. The odometer of a car reads 57321.0 km when the clock shows the time 08:30 AM. What is the distance moved by the car, if at 08:50 AM, the odometer reading has changed to 57336.0 km? Calculate the speed of the car in km/min during this time. Express the speed in km/h also.

6. Salma takes 15 minutes from her house to reach her school on a bicycle. If the bicycle has a speed of 2 m/s, calculate the distance between her house and the school.

7. Show the shape of the distance-time graph for the motion in the following cases:

    (i)   A car moving with a constant speed.

    (ii) A car parked on a side road.

8. Which of the following relations is correct?

    (i) Speed = Distance × Time

    (ii) Speed = $\dfrac{\text{Distance}}{\text{Time}}$

    (iii) Speed = $\dfrac{\text{Time}}{\text{Distance}}$

    (iv) Speed = $\dfrac{1}{\text{Distance} \times \text{Time}}$

9. The basic unit of speed is:

   (i)   km/min   (ii)   m/min

   (iii) km/h   (iv) m/s

10. A car moves with a speed of 40 km/h for 15 minutes and then with a speed of 60 km/h for the next 15 minutes. The total distance covered by the car is:

   (i)   100 km   (ii)   25 km

   (iii) 15 km   (iv) 10 km

11. Suppose the two photographs, shown in Fig. 13.1 and Fig. 13.2, had been taken at an interval of 10 seconds. If a distance of 100 metres is shown by 1 cm in these photographs, calculate the speed of the blue car.

12. Fig. 13.15 shows the distance-time graph for the motion of two vehicles A and B. Which one of them is moving faster?

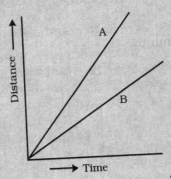

Fig. 13.15 *Distance-time graph for the motion of two cars*

13. Which of the following distance-time graphs shows a truck moving with speed which is not constant?

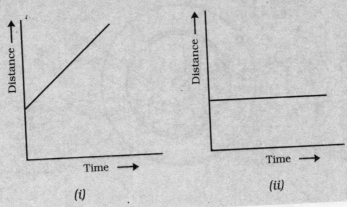

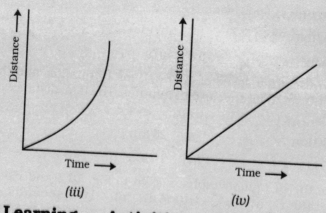

(iii)   (iv)

Extend Learning — Activities and Projects

1. You can make your own sundial and use it to mark the time of the day at your place. First of all find the latitude of your city with the help of an atlas. Cut out a triangular piece of a cardboard such that its one angle is equal to the latitude of your place and the angle opposite to it is a right angle. Fix this piece, called **gnomon**, vertically along a diameter of a circular board a shown in Fig. 13.16. One way to fix the gnomon could be to make a groove along a diameter on the circular board.

   Next, select an open space, which receives sunlight for most of the day. Mark a line on the ground along the North-South direction. Place the sundial in the sun as shown in Fig. 13.16. Mark the position of the tip of the shadow of the gnomon on the circular board as early in the day as possible, say 8:00 AM. Mark the position of the tip of the shadow every hour throughout the day. Draw lines to connect each point marked by you with the centre of the base of the gnomon as shown in Fig. 13.16. Extend the lines on the circular board up to its periphery. You can use this sundial to read the time of the day at your place. Remember that the gnomon should always be placed in the North-South direction as shown in Fig. 13.16.

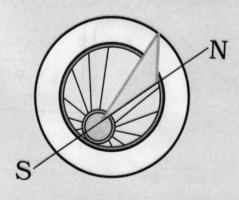

Fig. 13.16

2. Collect information about time-measuring devices that were used in the ancient times in different parts of the world. Prepare a brief write up on each one of them. The write up may include the name of the device, the place of its origin, the period when it was used, the unit in which the time was measured by it and a drawing or a photograph of the device, if available.

3. Make a model of a sand clock which can measure a time interval of 2 minutes (Fig. 13.17).

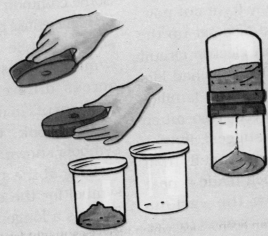

Fig. 13.17

4. You can perform an interesting activity when you visit a park to ride a swing. You will require a watch. Make the swing oscillate without anyone sitting on it. Find its time period in the same way as you did for the pendulum. Make sure that there are no jerks in the motion of the swing. Ask one of your friends to sit on the swing. Push it once and let it swing naturally. Again measure its time period. Repeat the activity with different persons sitting on the swing. Compare the time period of the swing measured in different cases. What conclusions do you draw from this activity?

Did you know?

The time-keeping services in India are provided by the National Physical Laboratory, New Delhi. The clock they use can measure time intervals with an accuracy of one-millionth of a second. The most accurate clock in the world has been developed by the National Institute of Standards and Technology in the U.S.A. This clock will lose or gain one second after running for 20 million years.

14 Electric Current and its Effects

You might have tried the game 'How steady is your hand?' suggested in Chapter 12 of Class VI. If not, you may try it out now. Paheli and Boojho had also set up the game by connecting an electric circuit as suggested in Class VI. They had lots of fun trying it out with their families and friends. They enjoyed it so much that they decided to suggest it to a cousin of theirs who stayed in a different town. So, Paheli made a neat drawing showing how the various electric components were to be connected (Fig.14.1).

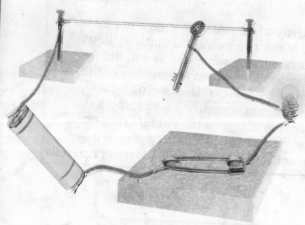

Fig. 14.1 *Setup to check how steady your hand is*

Can you draw this circuit conveniently? It made Boojho wonder if there was an easier way to represent these electric components.

14.1 Symbols of Electric Components

Some common electric components can be represented by symbols. In Table 14.1, some electric components and their symbols are shown. You may come across different symbols for these components in different books. However, in this book, we shall be using the symbols shown here.

Look at the symbols carefully. In the symbol for the electric cell, notice that there is a longer line and a shorter but thicker parallel line. Do you recall that an electric cell has a positive terminal and a negative terminal? In the symbol of the electric cell, the longer line represents the positive terminal and the thicker, shorter line represents the negative terminal.

For a switch the 'ON' position and the 'OFF' position are represented by the symbols as shown. The wires used to connect the various components in a circuit are represented by lines.

In Table 14.1, a battery and its symbol are also shown. Do you know what a *battery* is? Look at the symbol of a battery. Can you make out what a battery could be? For some of the activities we may need more than one cell. So, we connect two or more cells together as shown in Fig.14.2. Notice

Table 14.1 Symbols for some electric circuit components

S.No.	Electric component	Symbol
1.	Electric cell	⊣⊢
2.	Electric bulb	⊗
3.	Switch in 'ON' position	•—•
4.	Switch in 'OFF' position	•— ••
5.	Battery	⊣⊢⋯⊣⊢
6.	Wire	—

Many devices such as torches, transistors, toys, TV remote controls, use batteries. However, in some of these devices the electric cells are not always placed one after the other as shown in Fig. 14.2. Sometimes the cells are placed side by side. Then how are the terminals of the cells connected? Look carefully inside the battery compartment of any device. There is usually a thick wire or a metal strip connecting the positive terminal of one cell to the negative terminal of the next cell (Fig.14.3). In order to help you to place the cells correctly in the battery compartment, '+' and '–' symbols are usually printed there.

How can we connect the cells to prepare batteries for our activities? You may make a cell holder, as shown in Fig.14.4, using a wooden block, two iron strips and rubber bands. It is necessary

Fig. 14.2 (a) A battery of two cells (b) A battery of four cells

Fig. 14.3 Connecting two cells together to make a battery

that the positive terminal of one cell is connected to the negative terminal of the next cell. Such a combination of two or more cells is called a **battery**.

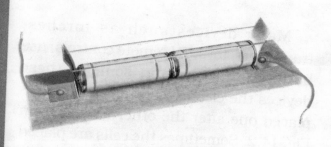

Fig. 14.4 A cell holder

Fig. 14.5 Holder for battery of two cells

that the rubber bands hold the metal strips tightly.

You could also buy cell holders from the market for making batteries of two or more electric cells. Place the cells in them properly, such that the positive

Paheli and Boojho wonder whether the batteries used in tractors, trucks and inverters are also made from cells. Then why is it called a battery? Can you help them to find the answer to this question?

Fig. 14.6 Truck battery and its cutout

terminal of one cell is connected to the negative terminal of the next cell. Connect a piece of wire each to the two metal clips on the cell holder as shown in Fig.14.5. Your battery is ready for use.

The symbol used for representing a battery is shown in Table.14.1.

Let us now draw a circuit diagram of an electric circuit using symbols shown in Table 14.1.

Activity 14.1

Make the electric circuit shown in Fig. 14.7. You used a similar circuit in Class VI to make an electric bulb glow. Do you remember that the bulb glows only when the switch is in the 'ON' position? The bulb glows as soon as the switch is moved to the 'ON' position.

Copy this electric circuit in your notebook. Make also a circuit diagram of this circuit using symbols for the various electric components.

Is your diagram similar to the one shown in Fig. 14.8?

It is much easier to draw a circuit diagram using symbols. Therefore, we generally represent an electric circuit by its circuit diagram.

Fig. 14.9 shows another circuit diagram. Is it identical to the circuit diagram shown in Fig.14.8? In which way is it different?

Would the bulb glow in this electric circuit? Recall that the bulb glows only when the switch is in the 'ON' position and the electric circuit is closed.

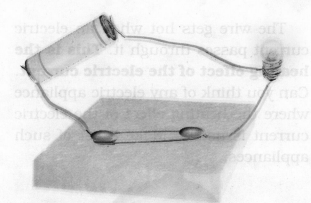

Fig. 14.7 *An electric circuit*

Fig. 14.8 *Circuit diagram of electric circuit shown in Fig. 14.7*

- Notice that the key or switch can be placed anywhere in the circuit.
- When the switch is in the 'ON' position, the circuit from the positive terminal of the battery to the negative terminal is complete. The circuit is then said to be closed and the current flows throughout the circuit instantly.
- When the switch is in the 'OFF' position, the circuit is incomplete. It is said to be open. No current flows through any part of the circuit.

In the bulb there is a thin wire, called the filament, which glows when an

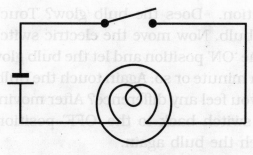

Fig. 14.9 *Another circuit diagram*

electric current passes through it. When the bulb gets fused, its filament is broken.

CAUTION

Never touch a lighted electric bulb connected to the mains. It may be very hot and your hand may get burnt badly. Do not experiment with the electric supply from the mains or a generator or an inverter. You may get an electric shock, which may be dangerous. Use only electric cells for all the activities suggested here.

If the filament of the bulb is broken, would the circuit be complete? Would the bulb still glow?

You might have noticed that a glowing electric bulb become warm. Do you know why?

14.2 HEATING EFFECT OF ELECTRIC CURRENT

Activity 14.2

Take an electric cell, a bulb, a switch and connecting wires. Make an electric circuit as shown in Fig.14.9. This activity has to be done using only one cell. Keep the switch in the 'OFF' position. Does the bulb glow? Touch the bulb. Now move the electric switch to the 'ON' position and let the bulb glow for a minute or so. Again touch the bulb. Do you feel any difference? After moving the switch back to the 'OFF' position, touch the bulb again.

Activity 14.3

Make a circuit as shown in Fig. 14.10. Take about 10 cm long piece of nichrome wire and tie it between the nails. (You can get nichrome wire from an electric repair shop or you can use a piece of discarded coil of an electric heater.) Touch the wire. Now switch on the current in the circuit by moving the switch to the 'ON' position. After a few

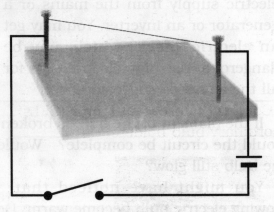

Fig. 14.10

CAUTION
Do not keep the switch in the 'ON' position for a long time, otherwise the cell may become weak very quickly.

seconds touch the wire. **(Do not hold it for a long time.)** Switch off the current. Touch the wire again after a few minutes.

The wire gets hot when an electric current passes through it. **This is the heating effect of the electric current**. Can you think of any electric appliance where the heating effect of the electric current is used? Make a list of such appliances.

You might have seen an electric room heater or an electric heater used for cooking. All these contain a coil of wire. This coil of wire is called an **element**. You may have noticed that when these appliances are switched on

Boojho could not see element in an electric iron. Paheli told him that electrical appliances, such as immersion heaters, hotplates, irons, geysers, electric kettles, hair dryers, have elements inside them. Have you ever seen the element in any appliance?

Fig. 14.11 Element of electric iron

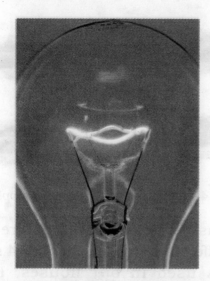

Fig. 14.12 Glowing filament of an electric bulb

after connecting to the electric supply, their elements become red hot and give out heat.

The amount of heat produced in a wire depends on its material, length and thickness. Thus, for different requirements, the wires of different materials and different lengths and thicknesses are used.

The wires used for making electric circuits do not normally become hot. On the other hand, the elements of some electric appliances become so hot that they are easily visible. The filament of an electric bulb gets heated to such a high temperature that it starts glowing.

If a large current passes through a wire, the wire may become so hot that it may even melt and break. But is it possible for a wire to melt and break? Let us check it out.

Activity 14.4

Make the circuit we used for Activity 14.3 again. However, replace the cell with a battery of four cells. Also, in place of

An electric bulb is used for light but it also gives heat. This is not desirable. This results in the wastage of electricity. This wastage can be reduced by using fluorescent tube lights in place of the bulbs. Compact fluorescent lamps (CFLs) also reduce wastage and can be fixed in the ordinary bulb holders.

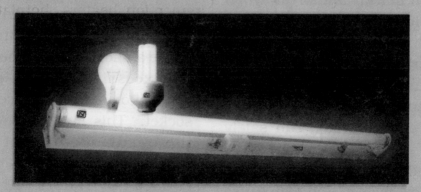

Fig. 14.13 Tube-lights and CFLs

However, before buying bulbs or tubes, or CFLs, look for the ISI mark of the Bureau of Indian Standards. In fact, before buying any electrical appliance, look for this mark. The ISI mark ensures that the appliance is safe and wastage of energy is minimum.

Fig. 14.14 *Fuse used in buildings*

Fig. 14.15 *Fuses used in electrical appliances*

the nichrome wire, tie a thin strand of steel wool. (The steel wool is commonly used for cleaning utensils and is available in grocery shops.) If there are any fans in the room, switch them off. Now pass the current through the circuit for sometime. Observe the strand of steel wool carefully. Note what happens. Does the strand of steel wool melt and break?

Wires made from some special materials melt quickly and break when large electric currents are passed through them. These wires are used for making **electric fuses** (Fig.14.14). In all buildings fuses are inserted in all electrical circuits. There is a maximum limit on the current which can safely flow through a circuit. If by accident the current exceeds this safe limit, the wires may become overheated and may cause fire. If a proper fuse is there in the circuit, it will blow off and break the circuit. A fuse is thus a safety device which prevents damages to electrical circuits and possible fires.

Fuses of different kinds are used for different purposes. Fig. 14.14 shows fuses used in our houses. Fuses shown in Fig. 14.15 are generally used in electrical appliances.

CAUTION

Never try to investigate an electric fuse connected to mains circuit on your own. You may, however, visit an electric repair shop and compare the burnt out fuses with the new ones.

One reason for excessive currents in electrical circuits is the direct touching of wires. This may happen if the insulation on the wires has come off due to wear and tear. This may cause a short circuit. Another reason for excessive current can be the connection of many devices to a single socket. This may cause overload in the circuit. You might have read reports in newspapers about fires caused by short circuits and overloads.

We observed the heating effect of the electric current and learnt how we use it to our advantage. Does the electric current have other effects also?

These days Miniature circuit breakers (MCBs) are increasingly being used in place of fuses. These are switches which automatically turn off when current in a circuit exceeds the safe limit. You turn them on and the circuit is once again complete. Look for ISI mark on MCBs also.

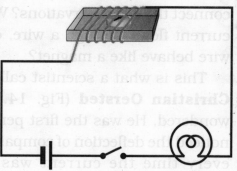

Fig. 14.16 Miniature circuit breaker (MCB)

CAUTION

Always, use proper fuses which have been specified for particular applications, carrying ISI mark. Never use just any wire or strip of metal in place of a fuse.

14.3 Magnetic Effect of Electric Current

Activity 14.5

Take the cardboard tray from inside a discarded matchbox. Wrap an electric wire a few times around the cardboard tray. Place a small compass needle inside it. Now connect the free ends of this wire to an electric cell through a switch as shown in Fig. 14.17.

Note the direction in which the compass needle is pointing. Bring a bar magnet near the compass needle. Observe what happens. Now, while watching the compass needle carefully, move the switch to the 'ON' position.

compass needle gets deflected when the current flows in a nearby wire. Can you connect these observations? When the current flows in a wire, does the wire behave like a magnet?

This is what a scientist called Hans Christian Oersted (Fig. 14.18) wondered. He was the first person to note the deflection of a compass needle every time the current was passed through the wire.

Fig. 14.17 Effect of current on a compass needle

through a wire, it behaves like a magnet. This is the magnetic effect of the electric current.

What do you observe? Does the compass needle deflect? Move the switch back to the 'OFF' position. Does the compass needle come back to its initial position?

Repeat the experiment a few times. What does this experiment indicate?

We know that the needle of a compass is a tiny magnet, which points in north-south direction. When we bring a magnet close to it, the needle gets deflected. We have also seen that

Fig. 14.18 Hans Christian Oersted (A.D. 1777-1851)

compass needle gets deflected when the current flows in a nearby wire. Can you connect the two observations? When the current flows through a wire, does the wire behave like a magnet?

This is what a scientist called **Hans Christian Oersted** (Fig. 14.18) also wondered. He was the first person who noticed the deflection of compass needle every time the current was passed through the wire.

So, when electric current passes through a wire, it behaves like a magnet. This is the magnetic effect of the electric current. In fact, an electric current can be used to make magnets. Do you find it too surprising? Let us try it out.

14.4 ELECTROMAGNET

Activity 14.6

Take around 75 cm long piece of insulated (plastic or cloth covered or enamelled) flexible wire and an iron nail, say about 6–10 cm long. Wind the wire tightly around the nail in the form of a coil. Connect the free ends of the wire

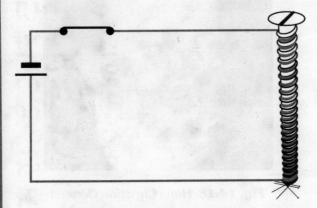

Fig. 14.19 *An electromagnet*

> Remember not to switch on the current for more than a few seconds at a time. The electromagnet weakens the cell quickly if left connected.

to the terminals of a cell through a switch as shown in Fig 14.19.

Place some pins on or near the end of the nail. Now switch on the current. What happens? Do the pins cling to the tip of the nail? Switch off the current. Are the pins still clinging to the end of the nail?

The coil in the above activity behaves like a magnet when electric current flows through it. When the electric current is switched off, the coil generally loses its magnetism. Such coils are called **electromagnets**. The electromagnets can be made very strong and can lift very heavy loads. Do you remember the crane about which you read in Chapter 13 of Class VI? The end of such a crane has a strong electromagnet attached to it. The electromagnets are also used to separate magnetic material from the junk. Doctors use tiny electromagnets to take out small pieces of magnetic material that have accidentally fallen in the eye. Many toys also have electromagnets inside them.

14.5 ELECTRIC BELL

We are quite familiar with an electric bell. It has an electromagnet in it. Let us see how it works.

Fig. 14.20 shows the circuit of an electric bell. It consists of a coil of wire wound on an iron piece. The coil acts as an electromagnet. An iron strip with a hammer at one end is kept close to the electromagnet. There is a contact screw near the iron strip. When the iron strip is in contact with the screw, the current flows through the coil which becomes an electromagnet. It, then,

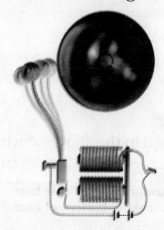

Fig. 14.20 *Circuit of an electric bell*

pulls the iron strip. In the process, the hammer at the end of the strip strikes the gong of the bell to produce a sound. However, when the electromagnet pulls the iron strip, it also breaks the circuit. The current through the coil stops flowing. Will the coil remain an electromagnet?

The coil is no longer an electromagnet. It no longer attracts the iron strip. The iron strip comes back to its original position and touches the contact screw again. This completes the circuit. The current flows in the coil and the hammer strikes the gong again. This process is repeated in quick succession. The hammer strikes the gong every time the circuit is completed. This is how the bell rings.

Keywords

Battery	Electric bell	Heating effect of current
Electric components	Electromagnet	Magnetic effect of current
Circuit diagram	Fuse	

What you have learnt

- It is convenient to represent electric components by symbols. Using these, an electric circuit can be represented by a circuit diagram.

- When an electric current flows through a wire, the wire gets heated. It is the heating effect of current. This effect has many applications.

- Wires made from some special materials melt quickly and break when large electric currents are passed through them. These materials are used for making electric fuses which prevent fires and damage to electric appliances.

- When an electric current flows through a wire, it behaves like a magnet.

- A current carrying coil of an insulated wire wrapped around a piece of iron is called an electromagnet.

- Electromagnets are used in many devices.

Exercises

1. Draw in your notebook the symbols to represent the following components of electrical circuits: connecting wires, switch in the 'OFF' position, bulb, cell, switch in the 'ON' position, and battery

2. Draw the circuit diagram to represent the circuit shown in Fig.14.21.

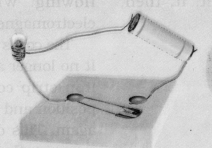

Fig. 14.21

3. Fig.14.22 shows four cells fixed on a board. Draw lines to indicate how you will connect their terminals with wires to make a battery of four cells.

Fig. 14.22

4. The bulb in the circuit shown in Fig.14.23 does not glow. Can you identify the problem? Make necessary changes in the circuit to make the bulb glow.

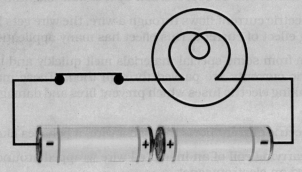

Fig. 14.23

5. Name any two effects of electric current.

6. When the current is switched on through a wire, a compass needle kept nearby gets deflected from its north-south position. Explain.

7. Will the compass needle show deflection when the switch in the circuit shown by Fig.14.24 is closed?

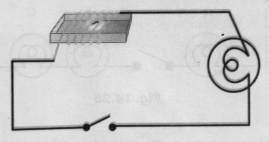

Fig. 14.24

8. Fill in the blanks:

    (a) Longer line in the symbol for a cell represents its _____terminal.

    (b) The combination of two or more cells is called a _____ .

    (c) When current is switched 'on' in a room heater, it _____ .

    (d) The safety device based on the heating effect of electric current is called a _____ .

9. Mark 'T' if the statement is true and 'F' if it is false:

    (a) To make a battery of two cells, the negative terminal of one cell is connected to the negative terminal of the other cell. (T/F)

    (b) When the electric current through the fuse exceeds a certain limit, the fuse wire melts and breaks. (T/F)

    (c) An electromagnet does not attract a piece of iron. (T/F)

    (d) An electric bell has an electromagnet. (T/F)

10. Do you think an electromagnet can be used for separating plastic bags from a garbage heap? Explain.

11. An electrician is carrying out some repairs in your house. He wants to replace a fuse by a piece of wire. Would you agree? Give reasons for your response.

12. Zubeda made an electric circuit using a cell holder shown in Fig. 14.4, a switch and a bulb. When she put the switch in the 'ON' position, the bulb did not glow. Help Zubeda in identifying the possible defects in the circuit.

13. In the circuit shown in Fig. 14.25

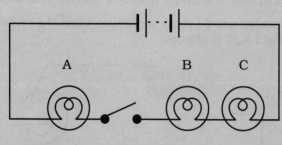

Fig. 14.25

(i) Would any of the bulb glow when the switch is in the 'OFF' position?

(ii) What will be the order in which the bulbs A, B and C will glow when the switch is moved to the 'ON' position?

Extended Learning — Activities and Projects

1. Set up the circuit shown in Fig. 14.17 again. Move the key to 'ON' position and watch carefully in which direction the compass needle gets deflected. Switch 'OFF' the current. Now keeping rest of the circuit intact, reverse the connections at the terminal of the cell. Again switch 'on' the current. Note the direction in which the needle gets deflected. Think of an explanation.

2. Make four electromagnets with 20, 40, 60 and 80 turns. Connect them one by one to a battery of 2 cells. Bring the electromagnet near a box of pins. Count the number of pins attracted by it. Compare the strengths of the electromagnets.

Paheli and Boojho saw a magic trick sometime back. The magician placed an iron box on a stand. He then called Boojho and asked him to lift the box. Boojho could easily lift the box. Now the magician made a show of moving his stick around the box while muttering some thing. He again asked Boojho to lift the box. This time Boojho could not even move it. The magician again muttered some thing and now Boojho could lift the box.

The audience, including Paheli and Boojho, were very impressed with the show and felt that the magician had some supernatural powers. However, after reading this chapter Paheli is wondering if the trick was indeed some magic or some science was involved? Can you guess what science might be involved?

3. Using an electromagnet, you can make a working model of a railway signal as shown in Fig.14.26.

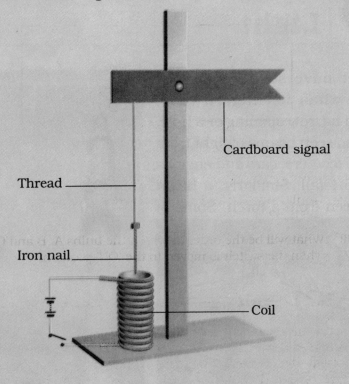

Fig. 14.26 *A working model of a railway signal*

4. Visit an electric shop. Request a mechanic to show you the various types of fuses and MCB and to explain how they work.

You can read more on the following website:

www.glenbrook.k12.il.us/gbssci/phys/class/circuits/u9l2a.html

Did You Know?

The credit for the invention of the electric bulb is usually given to Thomas Alva Edison, though others before him had worked on it. Edison was a remarkable man. He made some 1300 inventions including the electric bulb, gramophone, the motion picture camera and the carbon transmitter, which facilitated the invention of the telephone.

Fig. 14.27 *Thomas Alva Edison*
(A.D. 1847 – 1931)

15 | Light

You might have seen a beam of sunlight when it enters a room through a narrow opening or a hole. You may have also seen beams of light from the headlamps of scooters, cars and engines of trains [Fig. 15.1 (a)]. Similarly, a beam of light can be seen from a torch. Some of

(a) Rail engine

(b) Light house

Fig. 15.1 *Beams of light*

you may have seen a beam of searchlight from a light house or from an airport tower [Fig. 15.1 (b)].

What do these experiences suggest?

15.1 LIGHT TRAVELS ALONG A STRAIGHT LINE

Boojho recalls an activity he performed in Class VI. In that activity he looked

(a)

(b)

Fig. 15.2 *Looking at a candle through a straight and a bent pipe*

Fig. 15.3 *Reflection of objects in water*

Any polished or a shiny surface can act as a mirror. What happens when light falls on a mirror?

You have learnt in Class VI that a mirror changes the direction of light that falls on it. This change of direction by a mirror is called **reflection of light**. Can you recall the activity in which you got the light of a torch reflected from a mirror? Let us perform a similar activity.

Activity 15.1

Take a torch. Cover its glass with a chart paper which has three slits as shown in Fig. 15.5. Spread a sheet of chart paper

at a lighted candle first through a straight pipe and then through a bent pipe (Fig. 15.2). Why was Boojho not able to see the candle flame through a bent pipe?

This activity showed that light travels along straight lines.

How can we change the path of light? Do you know, what happens when light falls on a polished or a shiny surface?

15.2 REFLECTION OF LIGHT

One way to change the direction of light is to let it fall on a shiny surface. For example, a shining stainless steel plate or a shining steel spoon can change the direction of light. The surface of water can also act like a mirror and change the path of light. Have you ever seen the reflection of trees or buildings in water (Fig. 15.3)?

Paheli remembers the story of the lion and the rabbit from the *Panchtantra*, in which the rabbit fooled the lion by showing him his reflection in water (Fig. 15.4).

Fig. 15.4 *Reflection of the lion in water*

Fig. 15.5 *Reflection of light from a mirror*

on a smooth wooden board. Fix a plane mirror strip vertically on the chart paper (Fig. 15.5). Now direct the beam of light on the mirror from the torch with slits. Place the torch in such a way that its light is seen along the chart paper on the board. Now adjust its position so that the light from the torch strikes the plane mirror at an angle (Fig. 15.5).

Does the mirror change the direction of light that falls on it? Now move the torch slightly to either side. Do you find any change in the direction of reflected light?

Look into the mirror along the direction of the reflected light. Do you

see the slits in the mirror? This is the image of the slits.

This activity shows how light gets reflected from a plane mirror.

Let us play around with the images formed in mirrors and know a little more about them.

Activity 15.2

CAUTION
Handle the lighted candle with care. It is better if this activity is performed in the presence of a teacher or an elder person.

Place a lighted candle in front of a plane mirror. Try to see the flame of the candle in the mirror. It appears as if a similar candle is placed behind the mirror. The candle, which appears behind the mirror, is the **image** of the candle formed by the mirror (Fig. 15.6). The candle itself is the **object**.

Now move the candle to different positions in front of the mirror. Observe the image in each case.

Paheli wants to know, what makes things visible to us? Boojho thinks that objects are visible only when light reflected from them reaches our eyes. Do you agree with him?

Fig. 15.6 *Image of a candle in a plane mirror*

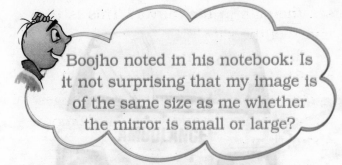

Boojho noted in his notebook: Is it not surprising that my image is of the same size as me whether the mirror is small or large?

Was the image upright in each case? Did the flame appear on top of the candle as in the object? Such an image is called **erect**. An image formed by a plane mirror is erect and of the same size as the object.

Now place a vertical screen behind the mirror. Try to obtain the image of the candle on this screen. Can you get the image on the screen? Now place the screen in front of the mirror. Can you get the image on the screen now? You will find that the image of the candle

cannot be obtained on the screen in either case.

What about the distance of the image from mirror? Let us perform another activity.

Activity 15.3

Take a chess board. If a chess board is not available, draw on a chart paper 64 (8×8) squares of equal size. Draw a thick line in the middle of the paper. Fix a plane mirror vertically on this line. Place any small object, such as a pencil sharpner, at the boundary of the third square counting from the mirror (Fig. 15.7). Note the position of the image. Now shift the object to the boundary of the fourth square. Again note the position of the image. Did you find any relation between the distance of the image from the mirror and that of the object in front of it?

Fig. 15.7 Locating image in a plane mirror

Paheli made a note in her notebook: In a plane mirror the image is formed behind the mirror. It is erect, of the same size and is at the same distance from the mirror as the object is in front of it.

You will find that the image is at the same distance behind the mirror as the object is in front of it. Now verify this by placing the object anywhere on the chart paper.

15.3 RIGHT OR LEFT!

When you see your image in a plane mirror, is it exactly like you? Have you ever noticed that there is one interesting difference between you and your image in a mirror? Let us find out.

Activity 15.4

Stand in front of a plane mirror and look at your image. Raise your left hand. Which hand does your image raise (Fig. 15.8)? Now touch your right ear. Which ear does your hand touch in your image? Observe carefully. You will find that in the mirror the 'right' appears 'left' and the 'left' appears 'right'. Note that only sides are interchanged; the image does not appear upside down.

Now write down your name on a piece of paper and hold it in front of a plane

Fig. 15.9 *An ambulance*

mirror. How does it appear in the mirror?

Boojho saw an ambulance on the road. He was surprised to see that the word 'AMBULANCE' in front was written in a strange manner.

Can you now understand why the word 'AMBULANCE' is written as in Fig. 15.9? When the driver of a vehicle ahead of an ambulance looks in her/his rear view mirror, she/he can read 'AMBULANCE' written on it and give way to it. It is the duty of every one of us to allow an ambulance to pass without blocking its way.

You might have observed that in the side mirror of a scooter or a car the images of all the objects appear smaller than the objects themselves. Have you ever wondered why it is so?

Fig. 15.8 *Left hand appears on the right side in the image*

15.4 PLAYING WITH SPHERICAL MIRRORS

Paheli and Boojho were waiting for their dinner. Boojho lifted a stainless steel plate and saw his image in it. Oh! This plate acts as a plane mirror. My image is erect and is of the same size. Paheli saw her image using the back of a steel spoon. "Boojho look here! I can also see my erect image though it is smaller in size. This spoon also acts as a mirror of some kind", said Paheli.

You can also use a spoon or any curved shining surface to see your image.

Activity 15.5

Take a stainless steel spoon. Bring the outer side of the spoon near your face and look into it. Do you see your image in it (Fig. 15.10)? Is this image different from what you see in a plane mirror? Is this image erect? Is the size of the image the same, smaller or larger?

Fig. 15.10 *Image from the outer side of a spoon*

Now look at your image using the inner side of the spoon. This time you may find that your image is erect and larger in size. If you increase the distance of the spoon from your face, you may see your image inverted (Fig. 15.11). You can also compare the image of your pen or pencil instead of your face.

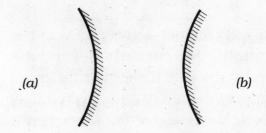

Fig. 15.11 *Image from the inner side of a spoon*

The curved shining surface of a spoon acts as a mirror. The most common example of a curved mirror is a spherical mirror.

If the reflecting surface of a spherical mirror is concave, it is called a concave mirror. If the reflecting surface is convex, then it is a convex mirror (Fig. 15.12).

Fig. 15.12 *A concave and a convex mirror*

Why are concave and convex mirrors called spherical mirrors?

Take a rubber ball and cut a portion of it with a knife or a hacksaw blade [Fig. 15.13 (a)]. **(Be careful. Ask an elder person to help you in cutting the ball).** The inner surface of the cut ball is called concave and the outer surface is called convex (Fig. 15.13 (b)).

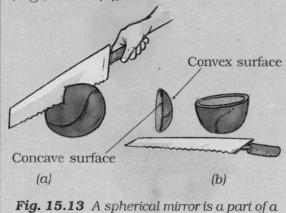

Convex surface

Concave surface

(a)   (b)

Fig. 15.13 *A spherical mirror is a part of a sphere*

The inner surface of a spoon acts like a concave mirror, while its outer surface acts like a convex mirror.

We know that the image of an object formed by a plane mirror cannot be obtained on a screen. Let us investigate if it is also true for the image formed by a concave mirror.

Activity 15.6

CAUTION

You will conduct Activity 15.6 in the sunlight. Be careful, never look directly towards the sun or its image as it may damage your eyes. You may look at the image of the sun when it is thrown on a screen or a wall.

Fig. 15.14 *A concave mirror forms a real image of the sun*

Take a concave mirror. Hold it facing the sun. Try to get the light reflected by the mirror on a sheet of paper. Adjust the distance of the paper until you get a sharp bright spot on it (Fig. 15.14). Hold the mirror and the sheet of paper steady for a few minutes. Does the paper start burning?

This bright spot is, in fact, the image of the sun. Notice that this image is formed on a screen. An image formed on a screen is called a **real image**. Recollect that in Activity 15.2 the image formed by a plane mirror could not be obtained on a screen. Such an image is called a **virtual image**.

Now let us try to obtain on the screen the image of a candle flame formed by a concave mirror.

Activity 15.7

Fix a concave mirror on a stand (any arrangement to keep the mirror steady would do) and place it on a table (Fig. 15.15). Paste a piece of white paper on a cardboard sheet (say about

Fig. 15.15 *Real images formed by a concave mirror*

15cm×10cm). This will act as a screen. Keep a lighted candle on the table at a distance of about 50 cm from the mirror. Try to obtain the image of the flame on the screen. For this, move the screen till a sharp image of the flame is obtained. Make sure that the screen does not obstruct the light from the candle falling on the mirror. Is this image real or virtual? Is it of the same size as the flame?

Now move the candle towards the mirror and place it at different distances from it. In each case try to obtain the image on the screen. Record your observation in Table 15.1. Is it possible to obtain the image on the screen when the candle is too close to the mirror (Fig. 15.16)?

We see that the image formed by a concave mirror can be smaller or larger in size than the object. The image may also be real or virtual.

Concave mirrors are used for many purposes. You might have seen doctors using concave mirrors for examining eyes, ears, nose and throat. Concave mirrors are also used by dentists to see an enlarged image of the teeth (Fig. 15.17). The reflectors of torches, headlights of cars and scooters are concave in shape (Fig. 15.18).

Fig. 15.16 *Virtual image formed by a concave mirror*

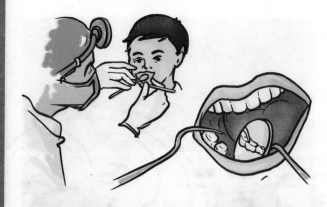

Fig. 15.17 *A dentist examining a patient*

Boojho observed his image in the shiny surface of the bell on his new bicycle. He found that his image was erect and smaller in size. He wondered

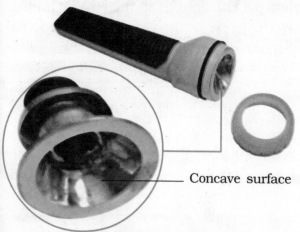

—— Concave surface

Fig. 15.18 *Reflector of a torch*

if the bell is also a kind of spherical mirror. Can you recognise the type of the mirror?

Note that the reflecting surface of the bell is convex.

Activity 15.8

Repeat Activity 15.7 now with a convex mirror in place of a concave mirror (Fig. 15.19). Record your observations in a Table similar to Table 15.1.

Could you get a real image at any distance of the object from the convex

Fig. 15.19 *Image formed by a convex mirror*

Table 15.1 Image formed by a concave mirror for object placed at different distances from it

Distance of the object from the mirror	Smaller/larger than the object	Character of the image	
		Inverted/ erect	Real/virtual
50 cm		...	...
40 cm		...	...
30 cm			
20 cm			
10 cm		...	
5 cm			

Fig. 15.20 *Convex mirror as side view mirror*

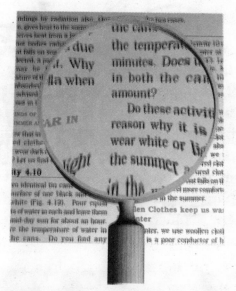

Fig. 15.21 *A magnifying glass*

mirror? Did you get an image larger in size than the object?

Can you now recognise the mirrors used as side mirrors in scooters? These are convex mirrors. Convex mirrors can form images of objects spread over a large area. So, these help the drivers to see the traffic behind them (Fig. 15.20).

15.5 IMAGES FORMED BY LENSES

You might have seen a magnifying glass. It is used to read very small print (Fig. 15.21). You might have also used it to observe the body parts of a cockroach or an earthworm. The magnifying glass is actually a type of a lens.

Lenses are widely used in spectacles, telescopes and microscopes. Try to add a few more uses of lenses to this list.

Get some lenses. Touch and feel them. Can you find some difference just by touching? Those lenses which feel thicker in the middle than at the edges are convex lenses [Fig. 15.22 (a)]. Those

which feel thinner in the middle than at the edges are concave lenses [Fig. 15.22 (b)]. Notice that the lenses are transparent and light can pass through them.

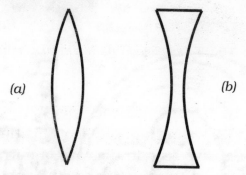

Fig. 15.22 *(a) A convex lens and (b) a concave lens*

Let us play with lenses.

CAUTION
It is dangerous to look through a lens at the sun or a bright light. You should also be careful not to focus sunlight with a convex lens on any part of your body.

Activity 15.9

Take a convex lens or magnifying glass. Put it in the path of sunrays. Place a sheet of paper as shown (Fig. 15.23). Adjust the distance between the lens and the paper till you get a bright spot on the paper. Hold the lens and the paper in this position for a few minutes. Does the paper begin to burn?

Now replace the convex lens with a concave lens. Do you see a bright spot

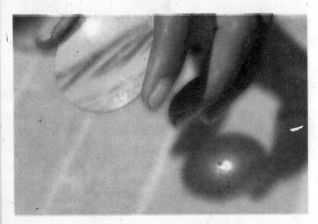

Fig. 15.23 *Real image of the sun by a convex lens*

on the paper this time, too? Why are you not getting a bright spot this time?

We have seen in the case of mirrors that for different positions of the object the nature and size of the image change. Is it true for lenses also?

Let us find out.

Activity 15.10

Take a convex lens and fix it on a stand as you did with the concave mirror. Place it on a table. Place a lighted candle at a distance of about 50 cm from the lens [Fig. 15.25 (a)]. Try to obtain the image

A convex lens converges (bends inward) the light generally falling on it [Fig. 15.24 (a)]. Therefore, it is called a converging lens. On the other hand, a concave lens diverges (bends outward) the light and is called a diverging lens [Fig. 15.24 (b)].

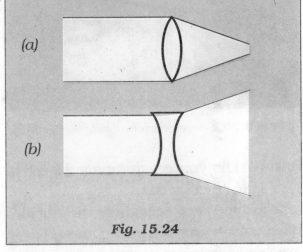

Fig. 15.24

of the candle on a paper screen placed on the other side of the lens. You may have to move the screen towards or away from the lens to get a sharp image of the flame. What kind of image did you get? Is it real or virtual?

Now vary the distance of the candle from the lens [Fig. 15.25 (b)]. Try to obtain the image of the candle flame every time on the paper screen by moving it. Record your observations as you did in Activity 15.7 for the concave mirror.

It means that we can see the image formed by a lens from the side opposite to that of the object.

(a)

(b)

Fig. 15.25 *Image by a convex lens for object placed at different distance from it*

Fig. 15.26 *Virtual image formed by the convex lens*

Fig. 15.27 *Image formed by a concave lens*

Did you get in any position of the object an image which was erect and magnified (Fig. 15.26). Could this image be obtained on a screen? Is the image real or virtual? This is how a convex lens is used as a magnifying glass.

In a similar fashion study the images formed by a concave lens. You will find that the image formed by a concave lens is always virtual, erect and smaller in size than the object (Fig. 15.27).

15.6 SUNLIGHT — WHITE OR COLOURF

Have you ever seen a rainbow in the sky? You might have noticed that it appears usually after the rain when the sun is low in the sky. The rainbow is

Fig. 15.28 *A rainbow*

Fig. 15.29 *A CD placed in sun*

seen as a large arc in the sky with many colours (Fig. 15.28).

How many colours are present in a rainbow? When observed carefully, there are seven colours in a rainbow, though it may not be easy to distinguish all of them. These are — red, orange, yellow, green, blue, indigo and violet.

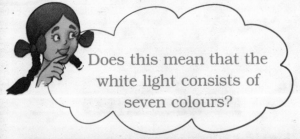

Does this mean that the white light consists of seven colours?

You might have seen that when you blow soap bubbles, they appear colourful. Similarly, when light is reflected from the surface of a Compact Disk (CD), you see many colours (Fig. 15.29).

On the basis of these experiences, could we say that the sunlight is a mixture of different colours? Let us investigate.

Activity 15.11

Take a glass prism. Allow a narrow beam of sunlight through a small hole in the window of a dark room to fall on one face of the prism. Let the light coming out of the other face of the prism fall on

Fig. 15.30 *A prism splits sunlight into seven colours*

Paheli wants to tell you that you can see a rainbow only when your back is towards the sun.

a white sheet of paper or on a white wall. What do you observe? Do you see colours similar to those in a rainbow (Fig. 15.30)? This shows that the sunlight consists of seven colours. The sunlight is said to be white light. This means that the white light consists of seven colours. Try to identify these colours and write their names in your notebook.

Can we mix these colours to get white light? Let us try.

Activity 15.12

Take a circular cardboard disc of about 10 cm diameter. Divide this disc into seven segments. Paint the seven rainbow colours on these segments as shown in Fig. 15.31 (a). You can also paste, coloured papers on these segments. Make a small hole at the centre of the disc. Fix the disc loosely on the tip of a refill of a ball pen. Ensure that the disc rotates freely [Fig. 15.31 (a)]. Rotate the disc in the daylight. When the disc is rotated fast, the colours get mixed together and the disc appears to be whitish [Fig. 15.31 (b)]. Such a disc is popularly known as Newton's disc.

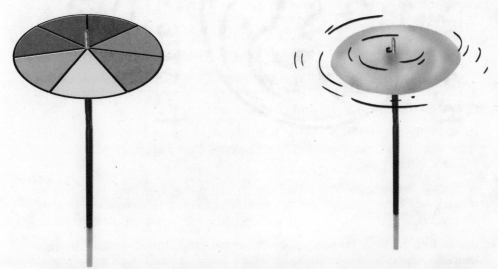

Fig. 15.31 *(a) A disc with seven colours (b) It appears white on rotating*

Paheli has a brilliant idea! She has prepared a small top with a small circular disc with seven rainbow colours painted on it (Fig. 15.32). When the top rotates it appears nearly white.

Fig. 15.32 *A top with seven colours*

Keywords

Concave lens

Concave mirror

Convex lens

Convex mirror

Erect image

Magnified image

Magnifying glass

Prism

Rainbow

Real image

Rear view mirror

Side mirror

Spherical mirror

Virtual image

What you have learnt

- Light travels along straight lines.

- Any polished or a shining surface acts as a mirror.

- An image which can be obtained on a screen is called a real image.

- An image which cannot be obtained on a screen is called a virtual image.

- The image formed by a plane mirror is erect. It is virtual and is of the same size as the object. The image is at the same distance behind the mirror as the object is in front of it.

- In an image formed by a mirror, the left side of the object is seen on the right side in the image, and right side of the object appears to be on the left side in the image.

- A concave mirror can form a real and inverted image. When the object is placed very close to the mirror, the image formed is virtual, erect and magnified.

- Image formed by a convex mirror is erect, virtual and smaller in size than the object.

- A convex lens can form real and inverted image. When the object is placed very close to the lens, the image formed is virtual, erect and magnified. When used to see objects magnified, the convex lens is called a magnifying glass.

- A concave lens always forms erect, virtual and smaller image than the object.

- White light is composed of seven colours.

Exercises

1. Fill in the blanks:

   (a) An image that cannot be obtained on a screen is called _____.

   (b) Image formed by a convex _____ is always virtual and smaller in size.

   (c) An image formed by a _____ mirror is always of the same size as that of the object.

   (d) An image which can be obtained on a screen is called a _____ image.

   (e) An image formed by a concave _____ cannot be obtained on a screen.

2. Mark 'T' if the statement is true and 'F' if it is false:

   (a) We can obtain an enlarged and erect image by a convex mirror. (T/F)

   (b) A concave lens always form a virtual image. (T/F)

   (c) We can obtain a real, enlarged and inverted image by a concave mirror. (T/F)

   (d) A real image cannot be obtained on a screen. (T/F)

   (e) A concave mirror always form a real image. (T/F)

3. Match the items given in Column I with one or more items of Column II.

Column I	Column II
(a) A plane mirror	(i) Used as a magnifying glass.
(b) A convex mirror	(ii) Can form image of objects spread over a large area.
(c) A convex lens	(iii) Used by dentists to see enlarged image of teeth.
(d) A concave mirror	(iv) The image is always inverted and magnified.
(e) A concave lens	(v) The image is erect and of the same size as the object.
	(vi) The image is erect and smaller in size than the object.

4. State the characteristics of the image formed by a plane mirror.

5. Find out the letters of English alphabet or any other language known to you in which the image formed in a plane mirror appears exactly like the letter itself. Discuss your findings.

6. What is a virtual image? Give one situation where a virtual image is formed.

7. State two differences between a convex and a concave lens.

8. Give one use each of a concave and a convex mirror.

9. Which type of mirror can form a real image?

10. Which type of lens forms always a virtual image?

Choose the correct option in questions 11–13

11. A virtual image larger than the object can be produced by a

    (i)   concave lens   (ii)   concave mirror

    (iii) convex mirror   (iv)   plane mirror

12. David is observing his image in a plane mirror. The distance between the mirror and his image is 4 m. If he moves 1 m towards the mirror, then the distance between David and his image will be

    (i)   3 m   (ii)   5 m

    (iii) 6 m   (iv)   8 m

13. The rear view mirror of a car is a plane mirror. A driver is reversing his car at a speed of 2 m/s. The driver sees in his rear view mirror the image of a truck parked behind his car. The speed at which the image of the truck appears to approach the driver will be

    (i)   1 m/s   (ii)   2 m/s

    (iii) 4 m/s   (iv)   8 m/s

Extended Learning — Activities and Projects

1. Play with a mirror

   Write your name with a sketch pen on a thin sheet of paper, polythene or glass. Read your name on the sheet while standing in front of a plane mirror. Now look at your image in the mirror.

2. A burning candle in water

   Take a shoe box, open on one side. Place a small lighted candle in it. Place a clear glass sheet (roughly 25 cm × 25 cm) infront of this candle (Fig. 15.33). Try to locate the image of the candle behind

Fig. 15.33 *Candle burning in water*

the glass sheet. Place a glass of water at its position. Ask your friends to look at the image of the candle through the sheet of glass. Ensure that candle is not visible to your friends. Your friends will be surprised to see the candle burning in water. Try to explain the reason.

3. Make a rainbow

Try to make your own rainbow. You can try this project in the morning or in the evening. Stand with your back towards the sun. Take a hosepipe or a water pipe used in the garden. Make a fine spray in front of you. You can see different colours of rainbow in the spray.

4. Visit a laughing gallery in some science centre or a science park or a village *mela*. You will find some large mirrors there. You can see your distorted and funny images in these mirrors. Try to find out the kind of mirrors used there.

5. Visit a nearby hospital. You can also visit the clinic of an ENT specialist, or a dentist. Request the doctor to show you the mirrors used for examining ear, nose, throat and teeth. Can you recognise the kind of mirror used in these instruments?

6. Role play

Here is a game that a group of children can play. One child will be chosen to act as object and another will act as the image of the object. The object and the image will sit opposite to each other. The object will make movements, such as raising a hand, touching an ear, etc. The image will have to make the correct movement following the movement of the object. The rest of the group will watch the movements of the image. If the image fails to make the correct movement, she/he will be retired. Another child will take her/his place and the game will continue. A scoring scheme can be introduced. The group that scores the maximum will be declared the winner.

You can read more on the following websites:

www.glenbrook.k12.il.us/gbssci/phys/mmedia/optics/ifpm.html

www.glenbrook.k12.il.us/gbssci/phys/class/refln/u13l1b.html

Did you know?

The mirrors can be used as weapons. Archimedes, a Greek scientist, is said to have done just that more than two thousand years ago. When the Romans attacked Syracuse, a coastal city-state in Greece, Archimedes used mirrors arranged as shown in Fig. 15.34. The mirrors could be moved in any direction. They were positioned such that they reflected the sunlight on the Roman soldiers. The soldiers were dazzled by the sunlight. They did not know what was happening. They got confused and ran away. This was an example of triumph of ideas over military might.

Fig. 15.34 Archimedes mirrors

16 Water: A Precious Resource

"Jal Hai, To Kal Hai"

"If you have water, you can think of the future"

You are perhaps aware that 22 March is celebrated as the **world water day**! A school celebrated 'water day' and invited posters from the children of your age group. Some of the posters presented on that day are shown in Fig. 16.1.

Fig. 16.1 *Collage of posters*

What is the message you get from these posters? Write your observations in your notebook and discuss them in the class.

Have you ever felt a shortage of water at home or at school? Your parents or teachers must very often be advising you not to waste water. No wonder we celebrate **water day** every year to attract the attention of everybody towards the importance of conserving water.

The amount of water recommended by the United Nations for drinking, washing, cooking and maintaining proper hygiene is a minimum of 50 litres per person per day. This amount is about two and a half buckets of water per person per day. Is your family getting at least this much of water? If yes, you should consider yourself fortunate because millions of people in our country do not get enough water. What about your friends and their families? Share your experience with them.

In some places there is an acute shortage of water. Taps running dry, long queues for water (Fig. 16.2), fights, marches and protests for demand of water have become a common sight, especially during summers. Some of the newspaper clippings shown in Fig. 16.3 clearly indicate this message. Is it not true that we face acute shortage of water?

Fig. 16.2 *Long queue for water*

Fig. 16.3 *Newspaper clippings*

Activity 16.1

Collect clippings from newspapers and magazines on the news items, articles and pictures related to water shortage. Paste them in your scrapbook and share it with your friends. List some problems faced by the people and discuss them in the class.

Water shortage has become a matter of concern throughout the world. It is estimated that in a few years from now

Fig. 16.4 *Earth appears blue from space*

 Year 2003 was observed as the International Year of Freshwater to make people aware of this dwindling natural resource.

more than one third of the people in the world could face water scarcity.

Before we discuss why water is getting scarce we must know how much water is available for use on our planet.

16.1 How much Water is Available

Look at the picture of the earth taken from space. Why does it appear blue? Surely, you can guess!

You are aware that about 71% of the earth's surface is covered with water. Almost all the water on the earth is contained in the seas and oceans, rivers, lakes, ice caps, as groundwater and in the atmosphere. However, most of this water is not fit for human consumption. The water that is fit for use is freshwater. Perform the following activity to estimate roughly the relative amount of water available in some of these sources.

Activity 16.2

Most of us assume water to be a limitless resource. From this activity can you

Steps	Figure	Remark
Take a medium-sized bucket and fill it up with water. It contains about twenty litres of water.		Assume that this water represents all the water present on the earth.
Take a tea spoon of about 5 mL capacity and transfer 100 spoons of water from the bucket to a small container, like a bath mug.		This represents total freshwater on the earth.
From the bath mug transfer thirty spoons of water to a glass tumbler.		This gives a measure of usable water present as ground-water.
Finally take out a quarter (1/4th) spoonfull of water from the mug.		It represents all the water present in all the lakes and rivers of the world.

- The water left in the bucket represents the saline water present in the seas, oceans and partly as groundwater. This water is not fit for human use.
- The water left in the bath mug represents the water, which is present in the frozen form in glaciers, ice caps and permanent snow; again not available readily.

Boojho wondered about the alarmingly small quantity of water available for our use.

Paheli quickly calculated and found that this amount is roughly 0.006% of all water found on the earth.

appreciate the actual amount of water available for human use? Does the finding worry you? Discuss this in your class.

16.2 FORMS OF WATER

Are you afraid that continuous use will some day exhaust all the water available for use? You know that water on the earth has been maintained for millions of years by various processes which make the **water cycle**. You have studied the water cycle in Class VI. Write in your own words what you know about the water cycle.

You know that when water circulates through the water cycle it can be found in all the three forms, i.e., solid, liquid and gas—at any given time somewhere on the earth. The **solid** form, snow and ice, is present as ice caps at the poles of the earth, snow-covered mountains and glaciers. **Liquid** water is present in oceans, lakes, rivers, and even underground. The **gaseous** form is the water vapour present in the air around us. The continuous cycling of water among its three forms keeps the total amount of water on the earth constant even when the whole world is using it. Does it give you any relief?

Can you recall the processes involved in water cycle? The following activity will help you.

Activity 16.3

Fig. 16.5 shows the processes involved in the water cycle. They are labelled by numbers. Match these numbers with the processes given in the jumbled form.

Most towns and cities have water supply system maintained by the civic

1. rudgon rawet

2. atooniaervp

3. acestoonnnid

4. duclos

5. tspratniaoinr

6. aitfinlronit

7. ntciepirtaipo

Fig. 16.5 *Water cycle*

bodies. The water is drawn from nearby lakes, rivers, ponds or wells. The water is supplied through a network of pipes. Many villages do not have such a water supply system. There people fetch water directly from the sources. Often women and children have to walk several kilometres to fetch water (Fig. 16.6). The children suffer a lot. They cannot attend school regularly since they spend hours in fetching water.

Fig. 16.6 *Women fetching water*

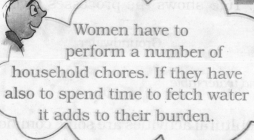

Women have to perform a number of household chores. If they have also to spend time to fetch water it adds to their burden.

A large number of people draw water from wells, tube wells or hand pumps. From where do these sources get water?

16.3 GROUNDWATER AS AN IMPORTANT SOURCE OF WATER

If we dig a hole in the ground near a water body we may find that the soil is moist. The moisture in the soil indicates the presence of water underground. If we dig deeper and deeper, we would reach a level where all the space between particles of soil and gaps between rocks are filled with water (Fig. 16.7). The upper limit of this layer is called the **water table**. The water table varies from

place to place, and it may even change at a given place. The water table may be at a depth of less than a metre or may be several metres below the ground. The water found below the water table is called groundwater. What is the source of this groundwater?

The rainwater and water from other sources such as rivers and ponds seeps through the soil and fills the empty spaces and cracks deep below the ground. The process of seeping of water into the ground is called **infiltration**. The groundwater thus gets recharged by this process. At places the groundwater is stored between layers of hard rock below the water table. This is known as an **aquifer**. Water in the aquifers can be usually pumped out with the help of tube wells or handpumps.

Have you ever been to a site where construction work is going on? From

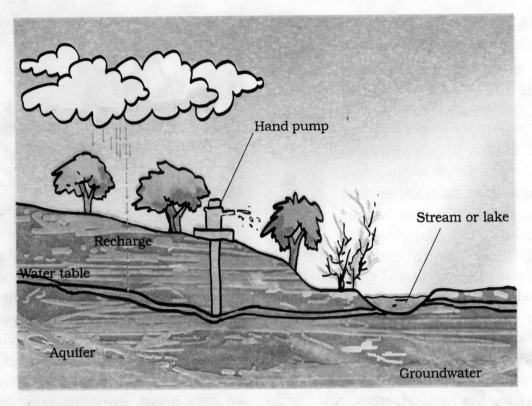

Fig. 16.7 *Groundwater and water table*

where do the workers get water for construction? May be you have seen boring being done at such sites to reach the water table. Enquire from the people working there how deep they have to dig.

Can we keep on drawing water from under the ground? How will it affect the water table?

16.4 DEPLETION OF WATER TABLE

Water drawn from under the ground gets replenished by seepage of rainwater. The water table does not get affected as long as we draw as much water as is replenished by natural processes. However, water table may go down if the water is not sufficiently replenished. This may happen due to many reasons. Increase in population, industrial and

agricultural activities are some common factors affecting water table. Scanty rainfall is another factor that may deplete the water table. Yet another factor affecting water table could be deforestation and decrease in the effective area for seepage of water.

Increasing population

Increasing population creates demand for construction of houses, shops, offices, roads and pavements. This decreases the open areas like parks, and playgrounds. This, in turn, decreases the seepage of rainwater into the ground. What could be the consequence? Recall that a *pukka* floor does not allow water to seep in easily, while in a grass lawn water seeps through in no time.

Moreover a huge amount of water is required for construction work. Often groundwater is used for this purpose.

So, on the one hand we are consuming more groundwater, and on the other we are allowing lesser water to seep into the ground. This results in depletion of water table. In fact, the water table in some parts of many cities has gone down to alarmingly low levels.

Increasing industries

Water is used by all the industries. Almost everything that we use needs water somewhere in its production process. The number of industries is increasing continuously. Water used by most of the industries is drawn from the ground.

Activity 16.4

Name some industries familiar to you. Make a list of the products obtained from these and used in our daily life. Discuss with your teacher and parents how the growing industrial activity is responsible for the depletion of water table.

Agricultural activities

A majority of farmers in India depend upon rains for irrigating their crops. Irrigation systems such as canals are there only in a few places. Even these systems may suffer from lack of water due to erratic rainfall. Therefore, farmers have to use groundwater for irrigation. Population pressure on agriculture forces increasing use of groundwater

day by day. This results in depletion of water table.

16.5 Distribution of Water

The distribution of water over the globe is quite uneven due to a number of factors.

Some places have good amount of rain and are water-rich. On the other hand, there are deserts which have scanty rainfall.

India is a vast country and the rainfall is not the same everywhere. Some regions have excessive rains while some others have very little rainfall. Excessive rains cause floods, whereas the absence of rains results in droughts. Therefore, some regions in our country may have floods while others may suffer from droughts at the same time.

Activity 16.5

Given here is the rainfall map of India (Fig. 16.8). It gives the average annual rainfall in different regions of our country.

- Locate on the map the place you live in.
- Are you blessed with sufficient rainfall?
- Is there sufficient water available in your area throughout the year?

It may be possible that we are living in an area where there is sufficient rainfall yet there is shortage of water. Can we attribute this to mismanagement of water resources?

16.6 Water Management

You have read in Class VI that in many places a regular supply of water is

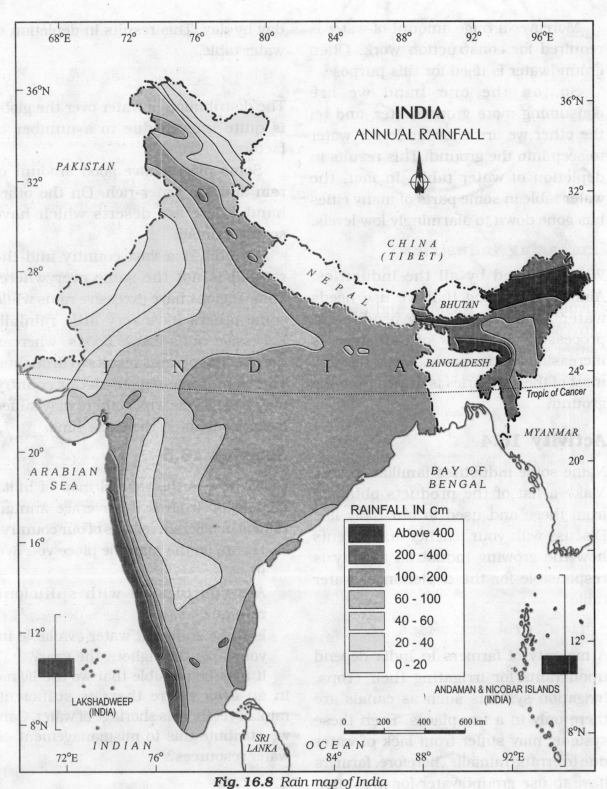

INDIA
ANNUAL RAINFALL

RAINFALL IN cm

	Above 400
	200 – 400
	100 – 200
	60 – 100
	40 – 60
	20 – 40
	0 – 20

LAKSHADWEEP
(INDIA)

ANDAMAN & NICOBAR ISLANDS
(INDIA)

0   200   400   600 km

Fig. 16.8 *Rain map of India*

1. Government of India, Copyright 2007.
2. Based upon Survey of India map with the permission of the Surveyor General of India.
3. The territorial waters of India extend into the sea to a distance of twelve nautical miles measured from the appropriate baseline.
4. The external boundaries and coastlines of India agree with the Record/Master Copy certified by Survey of India.

provided by a well-planned pipe system. When the civic authorities supply water through pipes not all of it may reach the destination. You might have seen water supply pipes leaking and a lot of water gushing out of the pipes. It is the responsibility of the civic authorities to prevent such wastage of precious water.

Mismanagement or wastage may take place at the level of individuals also. All of us, knowingly or unknowingly, waste water while brushing teeth, shaving, bathing, washing and during many other activities. Leaking taps is another source of huge water wastage. We waste water as though we do not need water the next time!

We have seen that most of the water that we get as rainfall just flows away. This is a waste of precious natural resource. The rainwater can be used to recharge the groundwater. This is referred to as **water harvesting** or **rainwater harvesting**, about which you have learnt in Class VI.

Find out if the buildings in your neighbourhood have water harvesting systems installed.

We have at many places in India an age old practice of water storage and water recharge like the **bawris**. *Bawri was the traditional way of collecting water.* With time the *bawris* fell into disuse and garbage started piling in these reservoirs. However, because of the acute water shortage, people in these areas have had to rethink. The *bawris* are being revived. Today the situation is that inspite of scanty rains these places are managing their water needs well.

A farmer using water in the field can also use water economically. Maybe you have heard of **drip irrigation** (Fig. 16.9). Drip irrigation is a technique of watering plants by making use of narrow tubings which deliver water directly at the base of the plant.

A case study

Bhujpur in the Kutch area of Gujarat has a very erratic rainfall. The only source of freshwater lies underground because rivers in this area do not have water throughout the year. Over the years, demand for water has grown. The withdrawal of groundwater has far exceeded recharge. As a result the water table has gone down alarmingly.

In 1989, the villagers along with a non-governmental organisation, decided to harvest rainwater. Eighteen check-dams were built on the Rukmavati river and its many tributaries. The water so collected increased percolation through the soil and recharged the aquifers.

According to farmers, the wells have water now and the water that flowed into the sea and was wasted has become available for irrigation.

Fig. 16.9 *Drip irrigation in a field*

16.7 WHAT ROLE YOU CAN PLAY

Have you ever shown concern if you saw a tap leaking in your house, school or any other place? Leaking taps waste a lot of water. You must make efforts to stop this leakage.

There are a number of ways you can adopt to minimise the wastage of water. Let us begin. We have given a few examples. Add on!

Water-wise habits

1. Turn off taps while brushing
2. Mop the floor instead of washing

16.8 EFFECT OF WATER SCARCITY ON PLANTS

You must have seen potted plants wilting and ultimately drying up if they did not get water even for a few days. You have already learnt in Chapter 1 that plants need water to get nutrients from the soil to prepare their food. Just imagine the consequences if water is not available to plants!

The green character of the planet shall be lost. This may mean the end of all life, for a world without plants shall mean no food, no oxygen, not enough rain, and innumerable other problems.

A successful initiative

Rajasthan is a hot and dry place. The challenge of natural scarcity of water was met by a successful experiment. A band of social workers has transformed a dry area in the Alwar district into a green place. They have revived five dried-up rivers — Arveri, Ruparel, Sarsa, Bhagani and Jahazwali by constructing water-harvesting structures.

Keywords

Aquifer	Groundwater	Water harvesting
Depletion	Infiltration	Water table
Drip irrigation	Recharge	

What you have learnt

- Water is essential for all living beings. There can be no life without it.

- Water exists in three forms: solid, liquid and vapour.

- Though water is maintained by the water cycle, yet there is an acute scarcity of water in many parts of the globe.

- There is an uneven distribution of water. Much of it has resulted from human activities.

- Rapid growth of industries, increasing population, growing irrigation requirements and mismanagement are some of the causes for water shortage.

- We need to be worried about the wastage during the supply of water through pipes, the leaking taps in buildings and other places. Unnecessary use of water and overdrawing from groundwater should be avoided. Recharge of water to the ground should be increased.

- The need of the hour is that every individual uses water economically.

- Plants wilt and ultimately dry-up if they are not watered for a few days.

Exercises

1. Mark 'T' if the statement is true and 'F' if it is false:

   (a) The freshwater stored in the ground is much more than that present in the rivers and lakes of the world. (T/F)

   (b) Water shortage is a problem faced only by people living in rural areas. (T/F)

   (c) Water from rivers is the only source for irrigation in the fields. (T/F)

   (d) Rain is the ultimate source of water. (T/F)

2. Explain how groundwater is recharged?

3. There are ten tubewells in a lane of fifty houses. What could be the long term impact on the water table?

4. You have been asked to maintain a garden. How will you minimise the use of water?

5. Explain the factors responsible for the depletion of water table.

6. Fill in the blanks with the appropriate answers:

   (a) People obtain groundwater through_____ and _____.

(b) Three forms of water are _____, _____ and _____.

(c) The water bearing layer of the earth is _____.

(d) The process of water seepage into the ground is called _____.

7. Which one of the following is **not** responsbile for water shortage?

(i) Rapid growth of industries

(ii) Increasing population

(iii) Heavy rainfall

(iv) Mismanagement of water resources

8. Choose the correct option. The total water

(i) in the lakes and rivers of the world remains constant.

(ii) under the ground remains constant.

(iii) in the seas and oceans of the world remains constant.

(iv) of the world remains constant.

9. Make a sketch showing groundwater and water table. Label it.

Extended Learning — Activities and Projects

1. Role play

You are a water detective in your school. You have a team of six members. Survey the campus and make a note of the following:

(a) Total number of taps

(b) Number of taps leaking

(c) Amount of water wasted due to leakage

(d) Reasons of leakage

(e) Corrective measures taken

2. Groundwater pumped out

Try to find out if there are any hand pumps in your neighbourhood. Go to the owner or the users of a few of these and find out the depth at which they struck water? If there are any differences, think of the probable reason. Write a brief report and discuss it in your class. If possible, visit a place where boring is going on to install a hand pump. Watch the process carefully and find out the depth of the water table at that place.

3. Catching rainwater — Traditional methods

Form groups of 4 to 5 students in the class and prepare a report on the various traditional ways of water harvesting. If possible, use the following web link: *www.rainwaterharvesting.org*.

4. Conservation of water

Carry out a campaign to conserve water at home and in the school. Design posters to remind others of the importance of water resources.

5. Create a logo

Hold a competition to create a logo or a symbol depicting water scarcity.

Did you know?

The importance of water management has been highlighted by a watershed management project near the village of Kothapally. The project has yielded dramatic results. Groundwater levels have risen, green cover has increased, and productivity and incomes in this semi-arid region have dramatically improved.

17 Forests: Our Lifeline

One evening Boojho entered the park with an elderly person. He introduced him to his friends. Prof Ahmad was a scientist working in the university. The children started playing while Prof Ahmad sat on a bench in the corner. He was tired as he had participated in the golden jubilee celebrations of the town. After a while, the children also came and sat around him. They wanted to know about the celebrations. Prof Ahmad told them that after the cultural programme, the senior people discussed the town's unemployment problem. A plan was proposed to put up a factory by clearing an area of the forest just outside the town. This would give the increasing population of the town a chance to get jobs. The children were very surprised when Prof Ahmad told them that many people had objected to this idea.

"This is because the forests serve as green lungs and water purifying systems in nature", Prof Ahmad explained. The children were confused. Prof Ahmad realised that the children had not visited a forest. The children also wanted to know more about the forest, so they decided to visit it with Prof Ahmad.

17.1 Visit to a Forest

One Sunday morning, the children packed a few things like a knife, a hand lens, a stick, a notebook and walked together through a forest trail near a village. On their way, they met Tibu, a young boy of their age group, of nearby village, who was taking cattle for grazing along with his aunt. He was very agile, running here and there to keep the herd together. When he saw the children, Tibu also started walking along with them, while his aunt went on a different path. As soon as they entered the forest Tibu raised his hand and signalled them to keep quiet because noise could disturb the animals living in the forest.

Tibu then took them to a place at a height to show them the broad view of the forest. Children were surprised because they could not see any land (Fig. 17.1). The different treetops had formed green cover over the land. However, the cover was not uniformly green. The

Fig. 17.1 *A view of a forest*

environment was peaceful and a cool breeze was blowing. This made children quite fresh and happy.

While coming down, they got excited on hearing a sudden sound of birds and some noise from the top branches of the trees. Tibu told them to relax since it was a normal phenomenon here. Because of the children's presence, some monkeys had climbed higher up on the trees where they disturbed the birds. Animals often give this type of warning call to alert other animals. Tibu also told that many other animals like boar, bison, jackals, porcupine, elephants live in the deeper areas of the forest (Fig. 17.2). Prof Ahmad cautioned children that they should not go deep into the forest.

Boojho and Paheli remembered that they have studied about forests as

Fig. 17.3 *Forest as habitat*

an example of a habitat in Class VI (Fig. 17.3). They could see now how the forest provides a home for many animals and plants.

Fig. 17.2 *Some forest animals*

Fig. 17.4 *Some forest plants*

The land where the children were walking was uneven and covered with many trees. Tibu helped them to identify *sal*, teak, *semal*, *sheesham*, *neem*, *palash*, fig, *khair*, *amla*, bamboo, *kachnar* (Fig. 17.4). Prof Ahmad pointed out that there are several other trees, shrubs, herbs and grasses in the forest. The trees were also covered with different types of creepers and climbers. The sun was barely visible through the leaves of the trees, making it quite dark inside the forest.

Activity 17.1

Observe the various things in your home and make a list of those which are made from material which may have been obtained from the forest.

You might have many wooden items on your list like plywood, fuel wood, boxes, paper, matchsticks, and furniture. Do you know that gum, oils, spices, fodder for animals and medicinal plants are also some of the products which we get from the forest (Fig. 17.5).

Sheila wondered who would have planted these trees. Prof Ahmad replied that in nature trees produce enough seeds. The forest floor provides favourable conditions for them to germinate and develop into seedlings

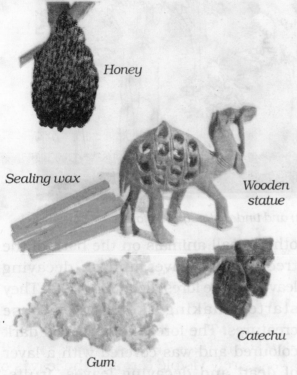

Fig. 17.5 *Forest products*

and saplings. Some grow up into trees. He added that branchy part of a tree above the stem is known as the **crown** of the tree (Fig. 17.6).

Prof Ahmad asked children to look up and observe how the branches of the tall trees look like a roof over the other plants in the forest. He told them that this is called a **canopy** (Fig. 17.7).

Activity 17.2

Visit a forest or a park in your neighbourhood. Observe the trees and try to identify them. You can take the help of some elders or books on trees. List the characteristics of the trees that you observe, such as the height, shape of leaves, crown, flowers, and fruits. Also draw the crowns of some trees.

Prof Ahmad pointed out that trees had crowns of different types and sizes. These had created different horizontal layers in the forest. These are known as understoreys (Fig. 17.7). Giant and tall trees constituted the top layer followed by shrubs and tall grasses, and herbs formed the lowest layer.

"Would we see similar kind of trees in every forest?"—asked Boojho. Prof Ahmad said, "No, due to different climatic conditions there are variations in the types of trees and other plants. The types of animals also differ from forest to forest."

Fig. 17.6 *Some crown shapes*

Canopy

Understorey

Fig. 17.7 *Canopy and under storeys in a forest*

A few children were busy watching beautiful butterflies fluttering here and there on the flowers of shrubs and herbs. They had a close look at the bushes. While doing that their hair and clothes had seeds and shrubs clinging to them.

They came across numerous insects, spiders, squirrels, ants and various other small animals on the bark of the trees, plant leaves and on decaying leaves on the forest floor (Fig. 17.8). They started making sketches of these creatures. The forest floor seemed dark coloured and was covered with a layer of dead and decaying leaves, fruits, seeds, twigs and small herbs. The decaying matter was moist and warm.

Children picked up various seeds and leaves for their collection. Walking over the dead leaf layer on the forest floor was like walking over a spongy carpet!

Is the decaying matter always warm? Prof Ahmad suggested that the children could perform an activity to get an answer to this question.

Activity 17.3

Dig a small pit. Put vegetable waste and leaves in it. Cover them with soil. Add some water. After three days, remove the

Fig. 17.8 *Forest floor*

upper layer of the soil. Does the pit feel warm inside?

Paheli asked, "There are so many trees here. Also, there are many forest like this. What difference will it make if we cut some trees for a factory?"

Prof Ahmad said, "You have read about autotrophs, heterotrophs and saprotrophs. You have learnt how green plants produce food. All animals, whether herbivores or carnivores, depend ultimately on plants for food. Organisms which feed on plants often get eaten by other organisms, and so on. For example, grass is eaten by insects, which in turn, is taken by the frog. The frog is consumed by snakes. This is said to form a food chain: Grass → insects → frog → snake → eagle. Many food chains can be found in the forest. All food chains are linked. If any one food chain is disturbed, it affects other food chains. Every part of the forest is dependent on the other parts. If we remove one component, say trees, all other components would be affected."

Prof Ahmad asked children to pick up leaves from the forest floor and observe them under a hand lens. They found tiny mushrooms over the

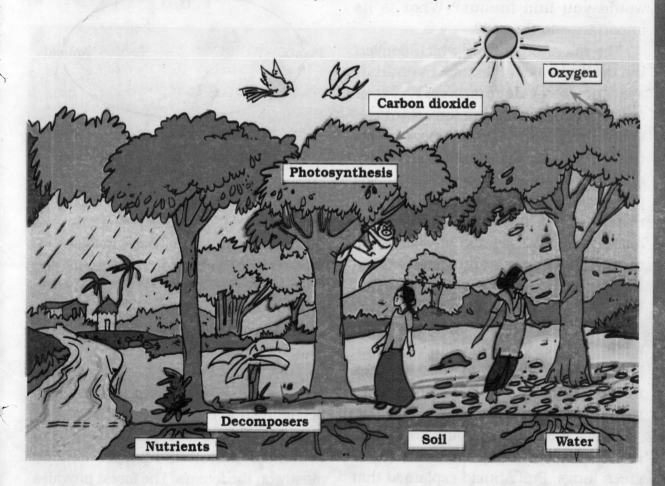

Fig. 17.9 *Interrelationship of plant, soil and decomposers in a forest*

decaying leaves. They also saw an army of tiny insects, millipedes, ants and beetle on them. They were wondering how these organisms live there. Prof Ahmad explained that apart from these animals which are easily seen, there are several organisms and micro-organisms that live in the soil. Paheli wondered what mushroom and other micro-organisms eat. Prof Ahmad replied that they feed upon the dead plant and animal tissues and convert them into a dark coloured substance called **humus**.

You have learnt about humus in Chapter 9. In which layer of the soil would you find humus? What is its importance to the soil?

The micro-organisms which convert the dead plants and animals to humus are known as **decomposers**. These micro-organisms play an important role in the forest. Soon, Paheli removed some dead leaves and discovered under them a layer of humus on forest floor. The presence of humus ensures that the nutrients of the dead plants and animals are released into the soil. From there, these nutrients are again absorbed by the roots of the living plants. "What happens if an animal dies in the forest?" Sheila asked. Tibu replied the dead animals become food for vultures, crows, jackals and insects." In this way, the nutrients are cycled. So, nothing goes waste in a forest (Fig. 17.9).

Paheli reminded Prof Ahmad that he had not explained why forests are called green lungs. Prof Ahmad explained that

plants release oxygen through the process of photosynthesis. The plants help to provide oxygen for animal respiration. They also maintain the balance of oxygen and carbon dioxide in the atmosphere (Fig. 17.10). That is why forests are called lungs.

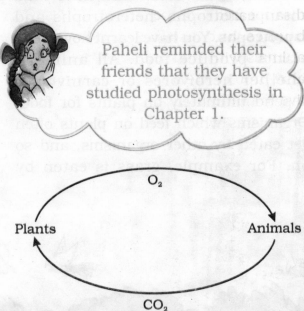

Paheli reminded their friends that they have studied photosynthesis in Chapter 1.

Fig. 17.10 *Balance of oxygen and carbon dioxide*

The children saw clouds forming in the sky. Boojho recalled what he had learnt about the water cycle in Class VI. Trees take in water from their roots and release water vapour into the air through evaporation.

If there were fewer trees, how will the water cycle be affected?

Tibu told them that the forest is not just home to plants and animals. Many people also live in the forest. Some of them may belong to different tribes. Tibu explained that these people depend mostly on the forests. The forest provides them with food, shelter, water and medicines. They have traditional knowledge about many medicinal plants in the forest.

While Boojho was drinking water from a small stream, he saw some deer crossing the stream (Fig. 17.11). They disappeared into the bushes. The dense bushes and the tall grass provide animals with the food and shelter. They also protect them from carnivores that live in the forest.

Fig. 17.11 *Deer in a forest*

Paheli remembered that she saw a Pipal sapling on the sidewall in her school. Can you help her to understand how this would have happened?

Tibu then started looking closely at the forest floor. Soon he called and showed the children droppings of some animals, and explained the difference between various types of droppings. Prof Ahmad informed them that the forest officers could recognise the presence of some animals in the forest by their droppings and footprints.

Boojho called every one and showed them a large, decaying heap of animal dropping. Several beetles and grubs were feeding on the heap and a bunch of seedlings was sprouting. "These seedlings are of the herbs and shrubs. The animals also disperse the seeds of certain plants and help the forest to grow

Fig. 17.12 *A sapling on a wall*

and regenerate. The decaying animal dung also provides nutrients to the seedlings to grow", said Prof Ahmad.

After listening to this, Boojho noted in his notebook, "By harbouring greater variety of plants, the forest provides greater opportunities for food and habitat for the herbivores. Larger number of herbivores means increased availability of food for a variety of carnivores. The wide variety of animals

Rain

Transpiration and evaporation

The closed canopy and many layers of vegetation slow down the speed of raindrops

Covered ground with decaying material acts like a sponge

The root system helps water to seep down into the ground

Water table

Fig. 17.13 *Rainwater drips from the trees and seeps into the ground*

helps the forest to regenerate and grow. Decomposers help in maintaining the supply of nutrients to the growing plants in the forest. Therefore, the forest is a **'dynamic living entity'** — full of life and vitality."

It was about afternoon and the children wanted to go back. Tibu

suggested another route for going back. While they were going back, it started raining. However, surprisingly, they saw that the raindrops were not hitting the forest floor directly. The uppermost layer of the forest canopy intercepted the flow of raindrops, and most of the water was coming down through the branches and the stems of the trees. From the leaves it was dripping slowly over branches of the shrubs and herbs (Fig. 17.13). They found that the ground was still dry. After about half an hour, the rain stopped. They noticed that the layer of dead leaves over the forest floor appeared wet now. But water did not stagnate in the forest.

Boojho thought that if it had rained so heavily in his town, it would have flooded the drains and roads.

What would happen if it rains heavily in your town?

Prof Ahmad told them that the forest also acts as a natural absorber of rainwater and allows it to seep. It helps maintain the water table throughout the year. Forests not only help in controlling floods but also help maintain the flow of water in the streams so that we get a steady supply of water. On the other hand, if trees are not present, rain hits the ground directly and may flood the area around it. Heavy rain may also damages the soil. Roots of trees normally bind the soil together, but in their absence the soil is washed away or eroded.

The children spent an hour at Tibu's village on their way back. The weather of the village was quite pleasant. Villagers told them that due to the surrounding forest, they receive good rainfall. The air also remained cool. Noise pollution, too is less because the forest absorbs the noise of the nearby highway.

The children learnt about the history of the village. It surprised them that the villages and the agricultural fields of that area were created after clearing the forest about sixty years ago. Tibu's grandfather told them that when he was young, the village was not as large as it was now. It was also surrounded by forests. Construction of roads, buildings, industrial development and increasing demand of wood created pressure on the forests and it started vanishing. He was not happy that the forest adjoining their village is not regenerating and is on the verge of disappearing due to overgrazing of animals and indiscriminate felling of trees. Prof Ahmad said that if we did things wisely we could preserve forests and environment as well as have development.

Children prepared a few pictures to show the consequences of such an event.

At the end of the visit, Prof Ahmad asked children to sum up the importance of forests. The children wrote: Forests provide us with oxygen. They protect soil and provide habitat to a large number of animals. Forests help in bringing good rainfall in neighbouring areas. They are a source of medicinal plants, timber and many other useful products. We must preserve our forests.

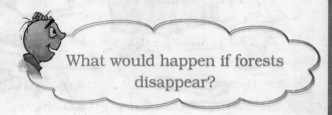

What would happen if forests disappear?

1. If forests disappear, the amount of carbon dioxide in air will increase, resulting in the increase of earth's temperature.
2. In the absence of trees and plants, the animals will not get food and shelter.
3. In the absence of trees, the soil will not hold water, which will cause floods.
4. Deforestation will endanger our life and environment. Think, what we can do to preserve our forests.

Keywords

Canopy	Deforestation	Seed dispersal
Crown	Humus	Soil erosion
Decomposers	Regeneration	Understorey

What you have learnt

- We get various products from the forests surrounding us.
- Forest is a system comprising various plants, animals and micro-organisms.
- In a forest, trees form the uppermost layer, followed by shrubs. The herbs form the lowest layer of vegetation.
- Different layers of vegetation provide food and shelter for animals, birds and insects.
- The various components of the forest are interdependent on one another.
- The forest keeps on growing and changing, and can regenerate.
- In the forest, there is interaction between soil, water, air and living organisms.
- Forests protect the soil from erosion.
- Soil helps forests to grow and regenerate.
- Forests are the lifeline for the forest-dwelling communities.
- Forests influence climate, water cycle and air quality.

Exercises

1. Explain how animals dwelling in the forest help it grow and regenerate.
2. Explain how forests prevent floods.
3. What are decomposers? Name any two of them. What do they do in the forest?
4. Explain the role of forest in maintaining the balance between oxygen and carbon dioxide in the atmosphere.
5. Explain why there is no waste in a forest.
6. List five products we get from forests?

7. Fill in the blank:

   (a) The insects, butterflies, honeybees and birds help flowering plants in_____.

   (b) A forest is a purifier of_____ and _____.

   (c) Herbs form the _____ layer in the forest.

   (d) The decaying leaves and animal droppings in a forest enrich the _____.

8. Why should we worry about the conditions and issues related to forests far from us?

9. Explain why there is a need of variety of animals and plants in a forest.

10. In Fig. 17.15, the artist has forgotten to put the labels and directions on the arrows. Mark the directions on the arrows and label the diagram using the following labels:

    clouds, rain, atmosphere, carbon dioxide, oxygen, plants, animals, soil, roots, water table.

11. Which of the following is not a forest product?

    (i) Gum

    (ii) Plywood

    (iii) Sealing wax

    (iv) Kerosene

12. Which of the following statements is not correct?

    (i) Forests protect the soil from erosion.

    (ii) Plants and animals in a forest are not depedent on one another.

    (iii) Forests influence the climate and water cycle.

    (iv) Soil helps forests to grow and regenerate.

Fig. 17.15

13. Micro-organisms act upon the dead plants to produce

    (i)   sand   (ii) mushrooms   (iii) humus   (iv) wood

Extended Learning — Activities and Projects

1. The Department of Environment is to decide whether some portion of a forest in your area could be cleared for a housing complex. Write a letter to the department explaining your point of view as a concerned citizen.

2. Visit a forest. Here is a list of points that would make your visit more fruitful.

    (a)   Make sure that you have permission to go into the forest.

    (b)   Make sure that you can find your way around. Get a map and go along with some one who is familiar with the area.

    (c)   Keep a record of the things you see and do. Observations make the visit interesting. Sketches and photographs are useful.

    (d)   You may record bird calls.

    (e)   Collect different kinds of seeds or hard fruits like nuts.

    (f)   Try to recognise various types of trees, shrubs, herbs, etc. Make lists of plants from different places in the forest and of different layers. You may not be able to name all the plants, but it is worth recording and seeing where they grow. Make a record of approximate heights of plants, crown shape, bark texture, leaf size, and flower colour.

    (g)   Learn to recognise the animal's droppings.

    (h)   Interview the forest officials and the people of surrounding villages and other visitors.

You must never collect birds' eggs, and their nests should never be disturbed.

You can read more on the following website:

www.wild-india.com

Did you know?

In India the area under forest cover is about 21% of the total area. It had steadily been falling since independence. But people now seem to have realised the importance of the forest cover. Reports suggest that the area under forest cover has slightly increased in recent years.

18 Wastewater Story

All of us use water in our homes and make it dirty.

Dirty! Are you surprised?

Rich in lather, mixed with oil, black-brown water that goes down the drains from sinks, showers, toilets, laundries is dirty. It is called **wastewater**. This used water should not be wasted. We must clean it up by removing pollutants. Have you ever thought where the wastewater goes and what happens to it?

18.1 WATER, OUR LIFELINE

Clean water is a basic need of human being. Let us make a mindmap of the many uses of clean water.

Activity 18.1

(We have given one example of the use of clean water. You can add many more.)

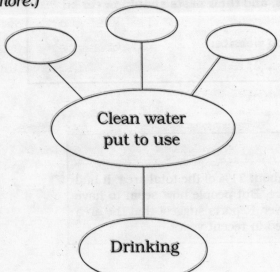

Clean water that is fit for use is unfortunately not available to all. It has been reported that more than one billion of our fellow human beings

WATER FOR LIFE
2005-2015

have no access to safe drinking water. This accounts for a large number of water-related diseases and even deaths. Women and girls walk for several kilometres to collect clean water, as you read in Chapter 16. Is it not a serious matter for human dignity?

You have studied in Chapter 16 about the increasing scarcity of fresh-water due to population growth, pollution, industrial development, mismanagement and other factors. Realising the urgency of the situation on the World Water Day, on 22 March 2005, the General Assembly of the United Nations proclaimed the period 2005–2015 as the International Decade for action on **"Water for life"**. All efforts made during this decade aim to reduce by half the number of people who do not have access to safe drinking water.

Cleaning of water is a process of removing pollutants before it enters a water body or is reused. This process of wastewater treatment is commonly known as "Sewage Treatment". It takes place in several stages.

18.2 What is Sewage?

Sewage is wastewater released by homes, industries, hospitals, offices and other users. It also includes rainwater that has run down the street during a storm or heavy rain. The water that washes off roads and rooftops carries harmful substances with it. Sewage is a liquid waste. Most of it is water, which has dissolved and suspended impurities. These impurities are called **contaminants**.

Activity 18.2

Locate an open drain near your home, school or on the roadside and inspect water flowing through it.

Record colour, odour and any other observation. Discuss with your friends and your teacher and fill up the following Table 18.1.

We know that sewage is a complex mixture containing suspended solids, organic and inorganic impurities, nutrients, saprotrophic and disease causing bacteria and other microbes.

Organic impurities	–Human faeces, animal waste, oil, urea (urine), pesticides, herbicides, fruit and vegetable waste, etc.
Inorganic impurities	– Nitrates, Phosphates, metals.
Nutrients	– Phosphorus and Nitrogen.
Bacteria	– Such as which cause cholera and typhoid.
Other microbes	– Such as which cause dysentery.

18.3 Water Freshens Up — An Eventful Journey

In a home or a public building generally one set of pipes brings clean water and another set of pipes takes away wastewater. Imagine that we could see through the ground. We would see a network of big and small pipes, called **sewers**, forming the **sewerage**. It is like a transport system that carries sewage from the point of being produced to the point of disposal, i.e. treatment plant.

Manholes are located at every 50 m to 60 m in the sewerage, at the junction

Table 18.1 Contaminant survey

S. No.	Type of sewage	Point of origin	Substances which contaminate	Any other remark
1.	Sullage water	Kitchen		
2.	Foul waste	Toilets		
3.	Trade waste	Industrial and commercial organisations		

of two or more sewers and at points where there is a change in direction.

Activity 18.3

Study the sewage route in your home/school/building. Do the following:

- Make a line diagram of the sewage route.
- Walk down the street or survey the campus to find the number of manholes.
- Follow an open drain and find out where it ends and which living organisms are found in and around it.

In case you do not have a sewerage system in your locality, find out how sewage is being disposed off.

Treatment of polluted water

Perform the following activity. It will help you understand the processes that take place at the wastewater treatment plant.

Activity 18.4

Divide yourself into groups to perform the activity. Record observations at each stage:

- Fill a large glass jar 3/4 full of water. Add some dirty organic matter such as grass pieces or orange peels, a small amount of detergent, and a few drops of an ink or any colour.
- Cap the jar, shake it well and let the mixture stand in the sun for two days.
- After two days, shake the mixture and pour a small sample into test tube. Label this test tube **"Before treatment; Sample 1"**. How does it smell?
- Use an aerator from an aquarium to bubble air through the sample in the glass jar. Allow several hours for aeration; leave the aerator attached overnight. If you do not have an aerator, use a mechanical stirrer or a mixer. You may have to stir it several times.
- The next day when aeration is complete, pour another sample into a second test tube. Label it as **"After aeration; Sample 2"**.
- Fold a piece of filter paper to form a cone. Wet the paper with tap water and then insert the cone in a funnel. Mount the funnel on a support (as you have learnt in Class VI).
- Place layers of sand, fine gravel and finally medium gravel in the funnel (Fig. 18.2). (An actual filtration plant does not use filter paper, but the sand filter is several metres deep).
- Pour the remaining aerated liquid through the filter into the beakers. Do not allow the liquid to spill over the filter. If the filtered liquid is not clear, filter it a few times till you get clear water.
- Pour a sample of the filtered water into a third test tube labelled **"Filtered; Sample 3"**.
- Pour another sample of the filtered water into a fourth test tube. Add a small piece of a chlorine tablet. Mix well until the water is clear. Label the test tube **"Chlorinated; Sample 4"**.

Fig. 18.2 Filtration process

Fig. 18.3 Bar screen

- Observe carefully the samples in all the test tubes. **Do not taste!** Just smell them!

    Now answer the following questions:

(a) What changes did you observe in the appearance of the liquid after aeration?

(b) Did aeration change the odour?

(c) What was removed by the sand filter?

(d) Did chlorine remove the colour?

(e) Did chlorine have an odour? Was it worse than that of the wastewater?

18.4 Wastewater Treatment Plant (WWTP)

Treatment of wastewater involves physical, chemical, and biological processes, which remove physical, chemical and biological matter that contaminates the wastewater.

1. Wastewater is passed through bar screens. Large objects like rags, sticks, cans, plastic packets, napkins are removed (Fig. 18.3).

2. Water then goes to a grit and sand removal tank. The speed of the incoming wastewater is decreased to allow sand, grit and pebbles to settle down (Fig. 18.4).

Fig. 18.4 Grit and sand removal tank

3. The water is then allowed to settle in a large tank which is sloped towards the middle. Solids like faeces settle at the bottom and are removed with a scraper. This is the **sludge**. A skimmer removes the floatable solids like oil and grease. Water so cleared is called clarified water (Fig. 18.5).

Fig. 18.5 *Water clarifer*

The sludge is transferred to a separate tank where it is decomposed by the anaerobic bacteria. The biogas produced in the process can be used as fuel or can be used to produce electricity.

4. Air is pumped into the clarified water to help aerobic bacteria to grow. Bacteria consume human waste, food waste, soaps and other unwanted matter still remaining in clarified water (Fig. 18.6).

After several hours, the suspended microbes settle at the bottom of the tank as activated sludge. The water is then removed from the top.

Fig. 18.6 *Aerator*

The activated sludge is about 97% water. The water is removed by sand drying beds or machines. Dried sludge is used as manure, returning organic matter and nutrients to the soil.

The treated water has a very low level of organic material and suspended matter. It is discharged into a sea, a river or into the ground. Nature cleans it up further. Sometimes it may be necessary to disinfect water with chemicals like chlorine and ozone before releasing it into the distribution system.

Become an active citizen

Waste generation is a natural part of human activity. But we can limit the type of waste and quantity of waste produced. Often we have been repelled by offensive smell. The sight of open drains is disgusting. The situation

> The water in a river is cleaned naturally by processes that are similar to those adopted in a wastewater treatment plant.

Did you know ?

It has been suggested that we should plant eucalyptus trees all along sewage ponds. These trees absorb all surplus wastewater rapidly and release pure water vapour into the atmosphere.

worsens in the rainy season when the drains start overflowing. We have to wade through the mud pools on the roads. Most unhygienic and unsanitary conditions prevail. Flies, mosquitoes and other insects breed in it.

You can be an enlightened citizen and approach the municipality or the gram panchayat. Insist that the open drains be covered. If the sewage of any particular house makes the neighbourhood dirty, you should

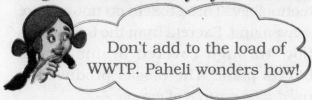

Don't add to the load of WWTP. Paheli wonders how!

request them to be more considerate about others' health.

18.5 BETTER HOUSE KEEPING PRACTICES

One of the ways to minimise or eliminate waste and pollutants at their source is to see what you are releasing down the drain.

- Cooking oil and fats should not be thrown down the drain. They can harden and block the pipes. In an open drain the fats clog the soil pores reducing its effectiveness in filtering water. Throw oil and fats in the dustbin.

- Chemicals like paints, solvents, insecticides, motor oil, medicines may kill microbes that help purify water. So do not throw them down the drain.

- Used tealeaves, solid food remains, soft toys, cotton, sanitary towels, etc. should also be thrown in the dustbin (Fig. 18.7). These wastes choke the

Fig. 18.7 *Do not throw every thing in the sink*

drains. They do not allow free flow of oxygen. This hampers the degradation process.

18.6 SANITATION AND DISEASE

Poor sanitation and contaminated drinking water is the cause of a large number of diseases.

Let us look at our own country. A vast number of our people are still

Vermi-processing toilet

A design of a toilet in which humans excreta is treated by earthworms has been tested in India. It has been found to be a novel, low water-use toilet for safe processing of human waste. The operation of the toilet is very simple and hygienic. The human excreta is completely converted to vermi cakes — a resource much needed for soil.

without sewerage facilities. Where do they relieve themselves?

A very large fraction of our people defecates in the open, on dry riverbeds, on railway tracks, near fields and many a time directly in water. Untreated human excreta is a health hazard. It may cause water pollution and soil pollution. Both the surface water and groundwater get polluted. Groundwater is a source of water for wells, tubewells, springs and many rivers as you learnt in Chapter 16. Thus, it becomes the most common route for water borne diseases. They include cholera, typhoid, polio, meningitis, hepatitis and dysentery.

18.7 ALTERNATIVE ARRANGEMENT FOR SEWAGE DISPOSAL

To improve sanitation, low cost **onsite sewage** disposal systems are being encouraged. Examples are septic tanks, chemical toilets, composting pits. Septic tanks are suitable for places where there is no sewerage system, for hospitals,

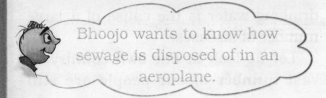

Bhoojo wants to know how sewage is disposed of in an aeroplane.

isolated buildings or a cluster of 4 to 5 houses.

Some organisations offer hygienic on-site human waste disposal technology. These toilets do not require scavenging. Excreta from the toilet seats flow through covered drains into a biogas plant. The biogas produced is used as a source of energy.

18.8 SANITATION AT PUBLIC PLACES

In our country fairs are organised periodically. A large number of people participate in them. In the same way railway stations, bus depots, airports, hospitals are very busy places. Thousands of people visit them daily. Large amount of waste is generated here. It must be disposed of properly otherwise epidemics could break out.

The government has laid down certain standards of sanitation but, unfortunately, they are not strictly enforced.

However, all of us can contribute in maintaining sanitation at public places. We should not scatter litter anywhere. If there is no dustbin in sight, we should carry the litter home and throw it in the dustbin.

Conclusion

We all have a role to play in keeping our environment clean and healthy. You must realise your responsibility in maintaining the water sources in a healthy state. Adopting good sanitation practices should be our way of life. As an agent of change your individual initiative will make a great difference.

Influence others with your energy, ideas and optimism. A lot can be done if people work together. There is great power in collective action.

Mahatma Gandhi said:

"No one need to wait for anyone else to adopt a humane and enlightened course of action."

Keywords

Aeration	Contaminant	Sewerage
Aerobic bacteria	Sanitation	Sludge
Anaerobic bacteria	Sewage	Wastewater
Biogas	Sewer	

What you have learnt

- Used water is wastewater. Wastewater could be reused.
- Wastewater is generated in homes, industries, agricultural fields and in other human activities. This is called sewage.
- Sewage is a liquid waste which causes water and soil pollution.
- Wastewater is treated in a sewage treatment plant.
- Treatment plants reduce pollutants in wastewater to a level where nature can take care of it.
- Where underground sewerage systems and refuse disposal systems are not available, the low cost on-site sanitation system can be adopted.
- By-products of wastewater treatment are sludge and biogas.
- Open drain system is a breeding place for flies, mosquitoes and organisms which cause diseases.
- We should not defecate in the open. It is possible to have safe disposal of excreta by low cost methods.

Exercises

1. Fill in the blanks:

    (a) Cleaning of water is a process of removing _____.

    (b) Wastewater released by houses is called _____.

    (c) Dried _____ is used as manure.

    (d) Drains get blocked by _____ and _____.

2. What is sewage? Explain why it is harmful to discharge untreated sewage into rivers or seas.

3. Why should oils and fats be not released in the drain? Explain.

4. Describe the steps involved in getting clarified water from wastewater.

5. What is sludge? Explain how it is treated.

6. Untreated human excreta is a health hazard. Explain.

7. Name two chemicals used to disinfect water.

8. Explain the function of bar screens in a wastewater treatment plant.

9. Explain the relationship between sanitation and disease.

10. Outline your role as an active citizen in relation to sanitation.

11. Here is a crossword puzzle: Good luck!

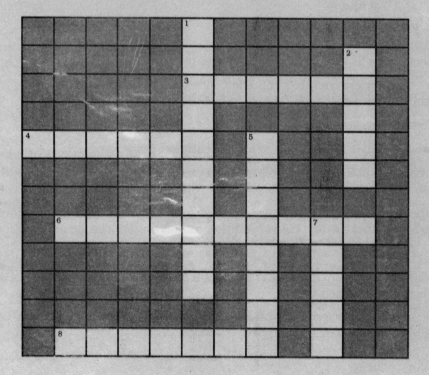

Across

3. Liquid waste products

4. Solid waste extracted in sewage treatment

6. A word related to hygiene

8. Waste matter discharged from human body

Down

1. Used water

2. A pipe carrying sewage

5. Micro-organisms which causes cholera

7. A chemical to disinfect water

12. Study the following statements about ozone:

   (a) It is essential for breathing of living organisms.

   (b) It is used to disinfect water.

   (c) It absorbs ultraviolet rays.

   (d) Its proportion in air is about 3%.

   Which of these statements are correct?

   (i) (a), (b) and (c)

   (ii) (b) and (c)

   (iii) (a) and (d)

   (iv) All four

Extended Learning — Activities and Projects

1. Construct a crossword puzzle of your own using the keywords.

2. Then and now: Talk to your grand parents and other elderly people in the neighbourhood. Find out the sewage disposal systems available to them. You can also write letters to people living in far off places to get more information. Prepare a brief report on the information you collected.

3. Visit a sewage treatment plant.

   It could be as exciting and enriching as a visit to a zoo, a museum, or a park. To guide your observation here are a few suggestions.

   Record in your notepad:

   Place _____   Date _____   Time _____

   Name of the official at the plant _____   Guide/Teacher _____

(a) The location of the sewage plant.

(b) Treatment capacity.

(c) The purpose of screening as the initial process.

(d) How is air bubbled through the aeration tank?

(e) How safe is the water at the end of the treatment? How is it tested?

(f) Where is the water discharged after treatment?

(g) What happens to the plant during heavy rains?

(h) Is biogas consumed within the plant or sold to other consumers?

(i) What happens to the treated sludge?

(j) Is there any special effort to protect nearby houses from the plant?

(k) Other observations.

For more information, consult:

Millennium Development Goals:

http://www.un.org/millenniumgoals/

"Water for Life" International Decade for Action:

http://www.un.org/waterforlifedecade/

World Water Day - Themes and Importance:

http://www.worldwaterday.org/

Through the ages Development of Sanitation:

http://www.sewerhistory.org/

*http://www.cep.unep.org/pubs/Techreports/tr43en/Household%
20systems.htm*

"By providing clean water and sanitation to the poorest people on the planet, we can reduce poverty and suffering and ensure education for all children." — UNICEF

An early engineering feat: Indus valley civilisation

One of the ancient civilisations, Harappa and Mohenjodaro had perhaps the world's first urban sanitation system. Within the city individual houses, or groups of houses, obtained water from wells. There was a separate room for bathing, and wastewater was directed to the covered drains which lined the major streets. The oldest toilet made of bricks is about 4500 years old.

INDEX

Educated Girl
Nation's Progress, Society's Pride

Did you know?

* Women have won the nobel prize in different areas.

* Women have been astronauts.

* Women are running industries successfully.

* Women have successfully led countries as Prime Ministers and Presidents.

* Women are top-level managers, scientists, leaders, technocrats...

If they can do it, why not you?

Give Girls Their Chance !